Macmillan/McGraw-Hill Science

Simple Organisms and Viruses

AUTHORS

Mary Atwater
The University of Georgia

Prentice Baptiste
University of Houston

Lucy Daniel
Rutherford County Schools

Jay Hackett
University of Northern Colorado

Richard Moyer
University of Michigan, Dearborn

Carol Takemoto
Los Angeles Unified School District

Nancy Wilson
Sacramento Unified School District

Macmillan/McGraw-Hill School Publishing Company
New York   Columbus

Fungi growing on a log

MACMILLAN / McGRAW-HILL

SCIENCE TURNS MINDS ON ™

CONSULTANTS

Assessment:
Mary Hamm
Associate Professor
Department of Elementary Education
San Francisco State University
San Francisco, CA

Cognitive Development:
Pat Guild, Ed.D.
Director, Graduate Programs in Education and
Learning Styles Consultant
Antioch University
Seattle, WA

Kathi Hand, M.A.Ed.
Middle School Teacher and Learning Styles Consultant
Assumption School
Seattle, WA

Derrick R. Lavoie
Assistant Professor of Science Education
Montana State University
Bozeman, MT

Earth Science:
David G. Futch
Associate Professor of Biology
San Diego State University
San Diego, CA

Dr. Shadia Rifai Habbal
Harvard-Smithsonian Center for Astrophysics
Cambridge, MA

Tom Murphree, Ph.D.
Global Systems Studies
Monterey, CA

Suzanne O'Connell
Assistant Professor
Wesleyan University
Middletown, CT

Sidney E. White
Professor of Geology
The Ohio State University
Columbus, OH

Environmental Education:
Cheryl Charles, Ph.D.
Executive Director
Project Wild
Boulder, CO

Gifted:
Dr. James A. Curry
Associate Professor, Graduate Faculty
College of Education, University of Southern Maine
Gorham, ME

Global Education:
M. Eugene Gilliom
Professor of Social Studies and Global Education
The Ohio State University
Columbus, OH

Life Science:
Wyatt W. Anderson
Professor of Genetics
University of Georgia
Athens, GA

Orin G. Gelderloos
Professor of Biology and Professor of Environmental Studies
University of Michigan—Dearborn
Dearborn, MI

Donald C. Lisowy
Education Specialist
New York, NY

Dr. E.K. Merrill
Assistant Professor
University of Wisconsin Center—Rock County
Madison, WI

Literature:
Dr. Donna E. Norton
Texas A&M University
College Station, TX

Macmillan/McGraw-Hill School Division
10 Union Square East
New York, New York 10003
Printed in the United States of America

ISBN 0-02-276079-2 / 7

1 2 3 4 5 6 7 8 9 RRW 99 98 97 96 95 94

Mathematics:
Dr. Richard Lodholz
Parkway School District
St. Louis, MO

Middle School Specialist:
Daniel Rodriguez
Principal
Pomona, CA

Misconceptions:
Dr. Charles W. Anderson
Michigan State University
East Lansing, MI

Dr. Edward L. Smith
Michigan State University
East Lansing, MI

Multicultural:
Bernard L. Charles
Senior Vice President
Quality Education for Minorities Network
Washington, DC

Paul B. Janeczko
Poet
Hebron, MA

James R. Murphy
Math Teacher
La Guardia High School
New York, NY

Clifford E. Trafzer
Professor and Chair, Ethnic Studies
University of California, Riverside
Riverside, CA

Physical Science:
Gretchen M. Gillis
Geologist
Maxus Exploration Company
Dallas, TX

Henry C. McBay
Professor of Chemistry
Morehouse College and Clark Atlanta University
Atlanta, GA

Wendell H. Potter
Associate Professor of Physics
Department of Physics
University of California, Davis
Davis, CA

Claudia K. Viehland
Educational Consultant, Chemist
Sigma Chemical Company
St. Louis, MO

Reading:
Charles Temple, Ph.D.
Associate Professor of Education
Hobart and William Smith Colleges
Geneva, NY

Safety:
Janice Sutkus
Program Manager: Education
National Safety Council
Chicago, IL

Science Technology and Society (STS):
William C. Kyle, Jr.
Director, School Mathematics and Science Center
Purdue University
West Lafayette, IN

Social Studies:
Jean Craven
District Coordinator of Curriculum Development
Albuquerque Public Schools
Albuquerque, NM

Students Acquiring English:
Mario Ruiz
Pomona, CA

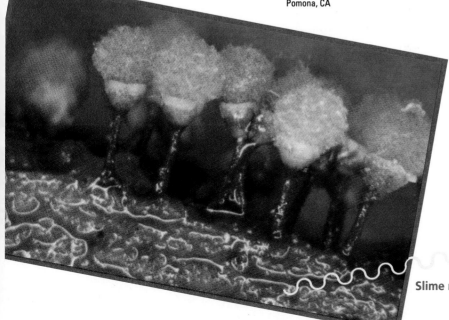

STUDENT ACTIVITY TESTERS

Alveria Henderson	Andrew Duffy
Kate McGlumphy	Chris Higgins
Katherine Petzinger	Sean Pruitt
John Wirtz	Joanna Huber
Sarah Wittenbrink	John Petzinger

FIELD TEST TEACHERS

Kathy Bowles
Landmark Middle School
Jacksonville, FL

Myra Dietz
#46 School
Rochester, NY

John Gridley
H.L. Harshman Junior High School #101
Indianapolis, IN

Annette Porter
Schenk Middle School
Madison, WI

Connie Boone
Fletcher Middle School
Jacksonville, FL

Theresa Smith
Bates Middle School
Annapolis, MD

Debbie Stamler
Sennett Middle School
Madison, WI

Margaret Tierney
Sennett Middle School
Madison, WI

Mel Pfeiffer
I.P.S. #94
Indianapolis, IN

CONTRIBUTING WRITER

William Netzer

Slime mold

Simple Organisms and Viruses

Lessons   Themes

Activities!

EXPLORE

TRY THIS

Features

Links

Literature Link

Math Link

Social Studies Link

Health Link

CAREERS

SCIENCE TECHNOLOGY AND Society

Focus on Environment

Focus on Technology

Departments

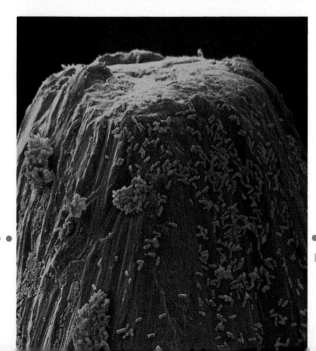

Bacteria on the end of a pin

Simple Organisms and Viruses

Can you guess what the relationship is between the White Cliffs of Dover pictured on this page and the smaller photographs on the right? Objects in these photos all come from cliffs like these. Would you have guessed what these cliffs were made of?

How do simple organisms interact with other living things? Do viruses interact with living things? How are the interactions of simple organisms and viruses important to environments everywhere on Earth?

The White Cliffs of Dover rise gracefully out of the sea on the coast of Great Britain and gleam white in the sun. They were formed from the remains of living things. Can you imagine how many organisms it took to make those cliffs? What do you think this rock from the cliffs is made of?

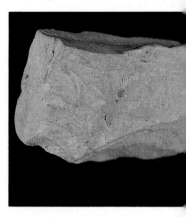

This is a piece of the White Cliffs of Dover

The last time you ate a slice of mushroom pizza, did you stop to think where the mushrooms came from? If you thought they were plants, like the green peppers or onions on your pizza, you were mistaken. Mushrooms are simple living things, related to the fuzzy growths that grow on old bread. Some of the foods you eat contain living things that are too small to be seen! Yogurt contains millions of microscopic living things that give it taste and texture.

Some of the things you can't see can cause problems instead of make your food taste good. Think of all the illnesses you have had—colds, flu, and infections. Some of these diseases are caused by living things and some by a particle called a virus (vī′ rəs). Some of the medicines you take to treat these diseases are produced by living things.

Recall that an organism is any living thing. The tiny living things that made up the cliffs, the mushroom, the living things in yogurt, and the living things that cause some illnesses are all simple organisms. In this unit you will explore how simple organisms and viruses compare with each other and other living things. Some are useful, even necessary for life, and others may be harmful to humans. Most live all around us, have no obvious effect on us, and we never know they are there.

209X

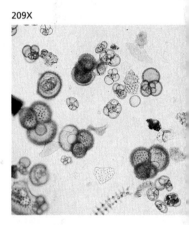

If you observed soil from the White Cliffs of Dover with a microscope, you would see shells from living things.

Minds On! You've already seen some places where some simple organisms and viruses are found and some of their effects on us. Can you think of any other places they can be found? What do they do there? In small groups, discuss how you think the world would be different without viruses and simple organisms.●

In this unit you will discover how simple organisms and viruses interact with living things to take care of their basic needs, and learn about their role in our environment.

Your teacher's chalk may have been made from deposits like the White Cliffs of Dover. A small piece can contain the remains of millions of living things.

Is There Life Beneath Your Feet?

You've seen some photographs of simple organisms and one of the places they can be found. Now you'll follow through the steps of an activity that will attempt to support a hypothesis about another place simple organisms might live. You'll also be learning about how scientists gather information and test their ideas in an organized way. This process often takes the form of a scientific method.

Although the term *scientific method* is used here, scientists do not all agree upon one scientific method. Rather, scientists pursue knowledge by recognizing and defining problems, formulating and testing hypotheses, making evaluations, and performing controlled investigations to collect data. To assist you in experimental investigations, a model for experimental design is presented for you.

Often you make observations and ask questions about what you have observed. Scientists do this, too. A question is posed in the form, "What do I want to find out about . . . ?" Then *a statement of the problem is written.* Our problem statement for the activity we are proposing is, "Are there organisms I can't see living in soil?"

A *hypothesis* (hī poth′ ə sis) answers the question, "What do I think the answer to my problem is?" You predict the answer based on what you already know about the subject. A hypothesis must be testable. Suppose that the hypothesis you form is, "There are living organisms in soil." Now you need to determine how you could test this hypothesis. How will you know if living things are present in soil? You know that not all living things can be seen. To detect them you need a characteristic that is common to all living things and is measurable.

You will need to *design the experiment* by using a process that proves the presence of living organisms and then use it to test whether there are living organisms in different soil types. You may recall that all living things give off carbon dioxide gas during the process of respiration. If it's possible to test for the presence of this gas, then you could use it as a means of testing your hypothesis. Scientists have discovered that the chemical bromothymol blue will undergo a change in color in the presence of carbon dioxide. You can use it to test types of soil for the presence of living organisms.

A variable is something in an experiment that can cause a change. In order to know whether the variable is the cause of the change, however, it's necessary to set up a control. A control is a standard against which to compare the results obtained when testing the variable. In this experiment, the variable will be the soil samples. The control is a sample of rice, a material that you know doesn't contain living organisms. You'll be looking at all samples to see if carbon dioxide gas is given off.

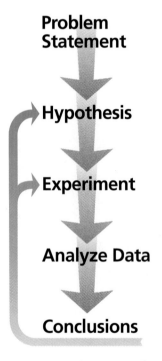

Problem Statement

Hypothesis

Experiment

Analyze Data

Conclusions

The steps of a scientific method

Scientists assemble materials and establish procedures before conducting an experiment. Read through the following materials and procedures that describe how you could test your hypothesis.

Scientists repeat experiments and compare data with other scientists to verify that their data are reliable. Results often lead to new questions.

What You Need

3 plastic bags; 4 cups each of garden soil, potting soil, and rice; 3/4 cup white sugar; 3 cups water; 3 labels; 3 stoppers with rubber tubes; 3 paper clamps; 3 test tubes; liquid bromthymol blue; 3 twist ties

What To Do

1. Add 4 cups of garden soil and 1/4 cup sugar to a plastic bag. Shake the bag to mix. Add 1 cup of water and mix again. Label the bag "garden soil."
2. Repeat step 1 with the potting soil and then with the rice.
3. Place a rubber stopper with a tube into the opening of each bag. Seal each bag around the stopper with a twist tie and press out most of the air. Place a paper clamp on each rubber tube.
4. Put the bags in a warm place overnight.
5. The next day, nearly fill 3 test tubes with bromthymol blue. Take each bag and put the open end of the tube into the liquid. Release the clamp and slowly squeeze the bag to release the trapped air. Note the color of the solutions in the test tubes.

As you do an experiment you have designed, you *record your observations, measurements, and the results.* In this experiment, you would note whether there had been a color change in the bromthymol blue that proved the existence of simple organisms in either soil. Remember that the rice mixture is a control.

Once a scientist has analyzed the data in an experiment, *a conclusion can be drawn* about the hypothesis that was made in answer to the problem statement. The conclusion will be based on the evidence gathered. Many times, however, the hypothesis will not be supported and the scientist will need to form a new hypothesis and begin again.

If you had done the experiment outlined here, the air from the rice sample wouldn't have produced a color change. You probably would have found that the air from the bag containing the garden soil caused the solution to turn bluish-green and that the air from the potting soil caused no color change.

Minds On! What conclusion might you have drawn from these results? Write your conclusion in your *Activity Log* on page 1.●

Science in Literature

How do simple organisms and viruses affect your life and the lives of people all over Earth? The books listed on these pages will describe the effects simple organisms and viruses have not only on your daily life, but also the environment and the course of history.

The Black Death
by James Day. New York: The Bookwright Press, 1989.

The Black Death, or bubonic plague, caused by the bacteria *Pasteurella pestis,* was responsible for the loss of 25 million lives from 1347 to 1351, and it continued to recur until the 17th century. The impact of the plague on European society was enormous. Large segments of populations were wiped out by this disease. James Day's book uses interesting details and reproductions of European artwork from the Middle Ages to give a personal slant to the tragic epidemic. The book describes the disease, how it was transmitted, and how the social and political conditions of the time affected its transmission. The plague also changed the social and political conditions of the time. Diseases don't just affect individuals, but society, and can change the course of history.

Sweetgrass

by Jan Hudson. New York: Scholastic Inc., 1984.

A Native American culture and how it is affected by a viral disease, smallpox, are vividly portrayed through the eyes of a teenage Blackfoot girl, Sweetgrass. Marriage is her only concern until the epidemic touches her family, and she is forced to hunt for food and nurse them through the illness. None of her friends and loved ones are left untouched, not even the young warrior she hopes to marry. The book allows you to experience firsthand the devastating effects smallpox had on many Native American groups, who had no immunity to smallpox.

Other Good Books To Read

Germs Make Me Sick

by Parnell Donahue, M.D. and Helen Capellaro. New York: Alfred A. Knopf, Inc., 1975.

What is it that *really* makes you sick? This book takes a look at some common diseases, how things that cause disease get into the body, and how doctors treat the diseases they cause. It also discusses how to stay well!

The Potato Eaters

by Karen Branson. New York: G.P. Putnam's Sons, 1979.

In 1846 a simple organism called a water mold wiped out most of the potato crop in Ireland. Widespread hunger and sickness resulted. This is the story of how one family copes with the disaster, and eventually comes to America seeking a better life.

Lichens

by Heather Angel. London: Angus & Robertson, 1980.

Lichens are unusual, tough, and important, but they often go unnoticed. You can use this book to explore common places where lichens can be found, and discover their role in your world.

Monerans- Friends or Enemies?

There is more happening in this farmer's field than you can easily observe. Do the photographs on the next page suggest an interaction between the beans and another living thing?

Minds On! Imagine that you had to live in a plastic garbage bag that was sealed at the top. How would you survive? In your *Activity Log* on page 2, describe what you might do to meet your needs.●

In your imaginary garbage bag, you were in a situation similar to a one-celled organism, bounded by a cell membrane. Though these organisms consist of only one cell, they live almost everywhere, including places people normally can't. One-celled organisms live in polar ice and in hot springs, in the ocean, and in places without oxygen or light.

These simple organisms are parts of environments you generally don't think about, because you can't see many of these organisms with the unaided eye. They can be found in such common places as on the skin, within the intestines, on tables and chairs, in clear bodies of water, in sewers, and on dust particles in the air. What do they do in those environments, and how do their actions affect us?

What living organisms do you see in the photograph of a farmer's field on the previous page? Recall the photographs of the White Cliffs of Dover and the experiment you read about in the Introduction to this unit. Take a look at the photographs to the right of this page. Could there be organisms present in the field that you can't see? Speculate how they might interact with the bean plants.

The organisms you'll read about in this lesson are necessary parts of all environments. No organism on Earth is unaffected by them. Sometimes the ways these simple organisms interact with other organisms are helpful—and sometimes harmful! In the Explore Activity on the next page, you'll discover another environment for these organisms, and how they affect it.

33X

There are nodules on the roots of peas, soybeans, alfalfa and bean plants.

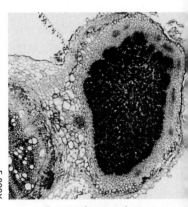

5,000X

A closer view shows the inside of a typical nodule.

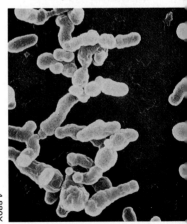

4,880X

These cells live in the nodule, but they are separate organisms! In this lesson you'll learn what they do there.

13

Activity!

Buttermilk Factories?

Have you ever tasted buttermilk or eaten buttermilk pancakes or biscuits? Simple organisms give buttermilk its distinctive taste. People who like to cook with or drink buttermilk think these organisms play a very helpful role in our lives! In this activity, you'll observe the simple organisms in buttermilk that give it its distinctive characteristics.

What You Need

cultured buttermilk
dropper
alcohol
jar, small
methylene blue
microscope
2 slides
Activity Log **pages 3–4**

What To Do

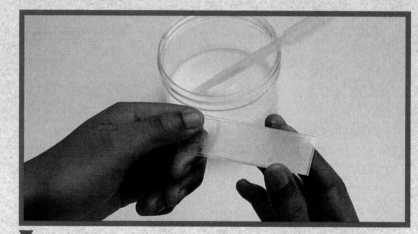

1 With the dropper, put 1 small drop of buttermilk on a clean slide. Spread out the drop with the edge of another clean slide so it forms a very thin layer of buttermilk. Allow the buttermilk on the slide to dry for a few moments. *Safety Tip:* Use care when handling breakable glass slides.

2 Fill a jar with alcohol.

3 When the slide has dried completely, place it into the jar of alcohol and leave it there for 10 min.

4 After 10 min, remove the slide and examine it under low power of the microscope.

Safety!

14   See the *Safety Tips* in steps 1 and 5.

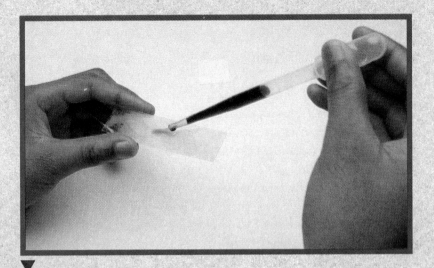

5 Place 2 or 3 drops of methylene blue on the slide. Wait 2 min, then carefully rinse off the excess dye by running the slide under a very gentle flow of cold water. Allow the slide to dry. *Safety Tip:* Methylene blue stains. Be careful not to get any on your skin, clothing, or tabletops.

6 Examine the slide under low power of the microscope. Draw any cells you see in your *Activity Log*.

What Happened?

1. What was the shape of the cells you observed? How were they grouped?
2. What was the purpose of the methylene blue?
3. What characteristics did the cells you observed have in common?

What Now?

1. What were the cells consuming for food?
2. Make a guess about how the cells cause buttermilk to taste different from regular milk.
3. How were these cells different from other cells you have seen? Did they have the same cell parts as other cells?
4. You have listed some similarities among the cells you observed and some ways these cells are different from other cells you've seen. Based on this information, what characteristics do you think the organisms described in this lesson will have?

What Are Monerans?

In the Explore Activity, what features did the cells you saw in the buttermilk have in common? How were they different from other cells you have seen? Recall that an animal or plant cell contains a nucleus and cell parts. Cell parts are called organelles. An example of an organelle is a chloroplast, the part of a plant cell where the process of food production takes place. Did you see a nucleus or organelles in the cells in buttermilk? The cells you observed in buttermilk were organisms classified in the Kingdom Monera. **Monerans** (mə nîr′ ənz) are one-celled organisms that lack a nucleus and organelles. Monerans have hereditary material, like other cells, but it's not contained within a nucleus. Your cat, the tree outside the window, the apple you ate yesterday, and your best friend are all made of cells that have a nucleus and cell parts called organelles. Monerans are the *only* organisms made of cells without a nucleus and organelles.

Even without organelles, monerans have the same basic life processes as other cells. They reproduce, grow, and break down food to provide energy in the process of respiration. These processes are carried out by molecules instead of organelles. The flavor of buttermilk comes from a substance produced by the organisms during respiration. The substance released by the monerans gives buttermilk its slightly sour taste, which regular milk doesn't have.

How are moneran and animal cells different? Monerans have cell walls, and don't have cell parts, or organelles. Although the scale in this illustration is not correct, you can observe that animal cells are larger than monerans.

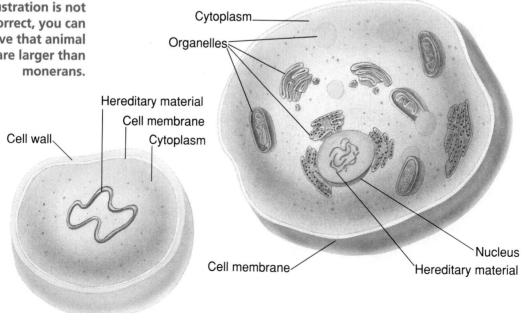

Cytoplasm

Organelles

Hereditary material

Cell membrane

Cytoplasm

Cell wall

Cell membrane

Nucleus

Hereditary material

Moneran

Animal Cell

You can't see the organisms living in buttermilk without a microscope because they consist of only one cell. Simple organisms that are too small to be seen with the unaided eye are called **microorganisms** (mī′krō or′gə niz′əmz). *Micro* is also part of the word *microscope*, and means "very small." An organism is any living thing. Microorganisms are not visible without a microscope because most consist of only one cell, like monerans. The cells of monerans are also smaller than individual plant or animal cells. Do the Math Link below to find out how small they are.

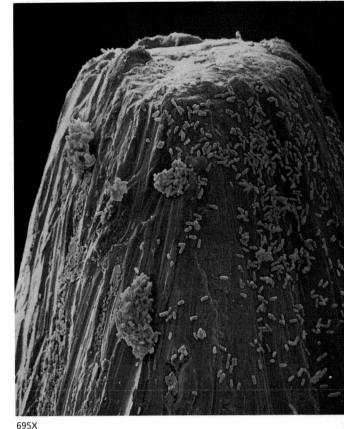

Monerans on the end of a pin

695X

Math 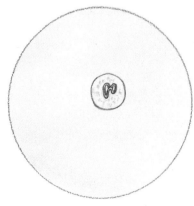 Link

Magnification

Can you calculate how large microorganisms actually are when you see them through a microscope? You can if you know how much the microscope is magnifying the image. The following drawings are representations of a moneran and a human cell seen through a microscope, magnified 2,000 times. With a metric ruler, measure the diameter of each cell. Record the sizes in your *Activity Log* on page 5. Divide each diameter by the magnification, 2,000. What is the actual size of each cell?

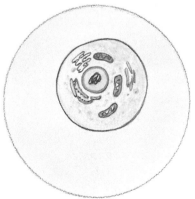

Human cell

Moneran

Did you see single cells and chains of cells in the buttermilk you observed? How can you explain this? You may have thought you were observing organisms made up of many cells, or that they were growing. But monerans are all one-celled organisms. The cells that work to give buttermilk its flavor are round, and sometimes link together in chains. Even though they clump together, the cells do not function as a system, with specialized jobs, the way cells in your body do. Your brain cells have a different job from your skin cells, but they both work to keep you alive and healthy. For monerans, each cell is an individual that survives on its own. These cells can be found in pairs, clumps, or chains.

Minds On! Why do you think the cells grow together? Explain your reasoning in your *Activity Log* on page 6.●

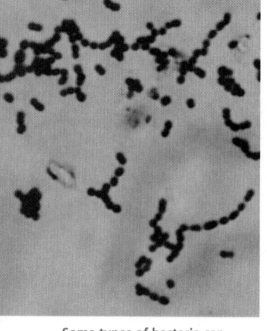

550X

Some types of bacteria can exist singly or in chains.

What Are Bacteria?

The Kingdom Monera is divided into two types of organisms, bacteria and cyanobacteria. **Bacteria** (bak tîr′ē ə) are monerans that consume food. The cells you saw in the buttermilk in the Explore Activity on pages 14 and 15 were bacteria. They were using the buttermilk as food. Bacteria in the soil and root nodules of the bean plants photographed on pages 12 and 13 were consuming material from decayed organisms.

Bacteria live in milk and in soil, in the air we breathe, and on all surfaces, including our skin. Did you determine the size of monerans by doing the Math Link on the previous page? Since monerans are microscopic, even smaller than animal cells, thousands of them live in every square centimeter we touch, even though we usually aren't aware of their presence.

The illustration on page 16 showed that all monerans have cell membranes and cell walls. The cell wall helps give the cell its shape and protect it. Some bacteria also have a sticky outer layer called a capsule. The capsule keeps the cell from drying out and helps the cell stick to its food source or other cells. Capsules help bacteria survive in a variety of environments.

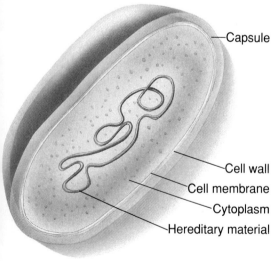

Capsule

Cell wall
Cell membrane
Cytoplasm
Hereditary material

A typical bacterial cell has a capsule.

Bacteria live everywhere. Although they can survive in many places, they can't live under all conditions. Bacteria need moisture, a certain temperature, and food to live. Although they can withstand a wide range of temperatures, most bacteria grow best when the temperature is around that of the human body, 37°C (98.6°F). Some types of bacteria normally live in ice. Others can survive temperatures near the boiling point. Most need oxygen, but some can live without oxygen, and others are killed by oxygen.

Like other living organisms, bacteria undergo the process of respiration. When oxygen is used to break down food into carbon dioxide and water, the process is called aerobic (â rō′ bik) respiration. Bacteria in soil produced carbon dioxide through the process of aerobic respiration in the experiment described on pages 8 and 9. Some bacteria have the ability to carry on respiration without oxygen. Respiration without oxygen is called anaerobic (an′â rō′bik) respiration. Anaerobic bacteria can be found in environments where bacteria that need oxygen can't survive.

Some bacteria, especially bacilli, can survive when conditions are not favorable for growth by forming structures called endospores. An endospore is a thick-walled structure that forms around the bacteria's hereditary material and a small amount of cytoplasm. The rest of the cell may die. Some endospores can withstand boiling, freezing, and very dry conditions for years. If conditions improve, the endospore develops into an active cell and will begin to reproduce again. During fission, the reproductive process of bacteria, hereditary material is copied and the cell divides into two identical cells. If conditions for reproduction are ideal, it's possible for fission to occur every 20 minutes in some bacteria.

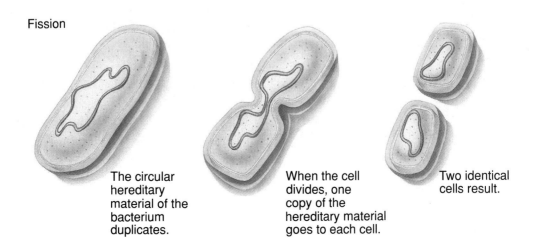

Fission

The circular hereditary material of the bacterium duplicates.

When the cell divides, one copy of the hereditary material goes to each cell.

Two identical cells result.

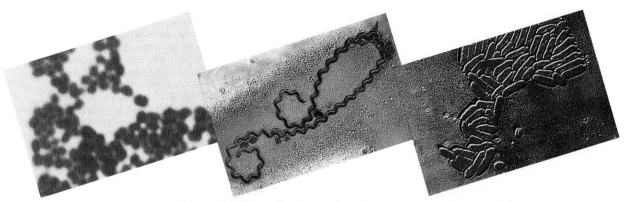

These photographs show the three common shapes of bacteria. Round bacteria are called cocci (kok′sī). Spiral-shaped bacteria are called spirilla (spī ril′ ə). Rod-shaped bacteria are called bacilli (bə sil′ ī). Which shape did the bacteria you observed in buttermilk in the Explore Activity on pages 14 and 15 have?

Activity!

Name This Bacterium

Bacteria have different shapes and are often described by their shape. In this activity you will use a key to determine how bacteria can be named and learn some characteristics of bacteria.

What You Need
Bacteria Identification Key
Activity Log page 7

Identify the shape of the cell or cells for the first bacteria illustrated below. Is it round, rod-shaped, or spiral? Go to the section of the identification key where it says "Start Here." Follow the instructions to go to the next section in the key. The section of the key to which you are directed will have additional characteristics of bacteria listed. Determine which one describes this type of bacteria. Follow the instructions in the key until you find the name of the species of bacteria. Write the name of the bacteria in your *Activity Log*. Follow the instructions in the key until you have named all the bacteria illustrated. Do you see any patterns to the way bacteria are named? How does their name relate to their shape? Write your answers in your *Activity Log*.

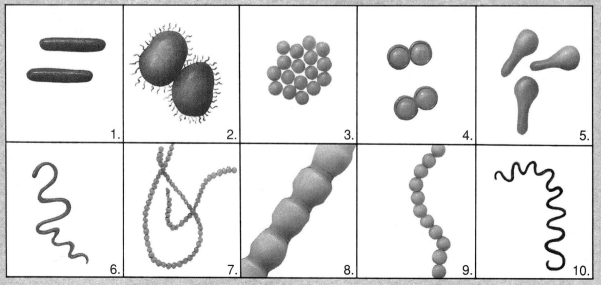

An Important Interaction—
Bacteria as Decomposers

Most bacteria are consumers—they acquire energy for survival and reproduction by consuming food. The fact that bacteria must take in food shapes their interactions with other organisms and their roles in their environments. Bacteria may feed on other living organisms or on dead organisms. Some bacteria get their energy by breaking down, or decomposing, dead materials.

Did you know that you are an environment for many bacteria, and that without them, you would have difficulty digesting food? Certain types of bacteria live in your intestines and decompose partially digested food. Bacteria also aid digestion in the stomachs of cows by decomposing grass so the cow can extract nutrients from it. Decomposers are very important parts of any environment—what would happen if nothing broke down dead plants and animals? Decomposers return minerals and other materials to the soil so they can be used by other organisms. Below, and on the next page, you will read how people use decomposing bacteria in sewage treatment plants and in compost piles to break down dead material.

Sewage treatment plants use bacteria to decompose waste material from people's homes. The sewage is often passed through a series of tanks as it's being decomposed. Some wastes are skimmed from the top of the water; others settle to the bottom and are drained off. Chemical treatment may also be used to purify the water. Clean, drinkable water is the end product.

Focus on Environment

Composting—What Bacteria Do Best!

Have you ever heard the word *biodegradable* (bī′ō di grā′ də bəl)? It describes materials that can be decomposed by bacteria and other simple organisms. Many of the products made by industry, such as foam and plastic, can't be broken down by bacteria. When we throw these items away, trash dumps fill up quickly. In some cities, landfills have closed because they were full. Today, more items are being produced to be biodegradable, so bacteria can do their job of decomposing. What items do you have at home that say they are biodegradable on the packaging?

Minds On! What are some ways you can save space in landfills? How can you use bacteria to help you save space? Discuss your ideas with your classmates. How many ideas can you put into practice in your life?●

Does your family buy fertilizer to put in a garden or on flower beds? You can have bacteria help you reduce your amount of trash and provide fertilizer by making a compost pile, a place set aside for decomposing garbage and yard wastes. There are containers that can be purchased for this purpose, but you can build one at home or school—with permission! An out-of-the-way area of your yard or school grounds can be used. With chicken wire and a few boards, make a fence about one meter high around an area about one meter across.

Pile dead leaves and plants in a heap inside the fence. Manure, garbage such as vegetable peelings or coffee grounds, or garden soil may be added. Be careful about what you put into your compost. If you use vegetable peelings that still have pesticides on them, or grass that has herbicides on it, these substances will end up in your fertilizer—and possibly in the food that uses the fertilizer! Washing vegetables should remove pesticides. Do not add meat products, since animals will be attracted by the smell! The bacteria present on the dead plants or in the manure, garbage, or soil will break down the dead matter and release nutrients. When added to soil, the compost is a good fertilizer.

Raw waste

Compost heap

Material produced by bacteria in compost heap

Bacteria Interact With Living Organisms

Did you speculate about any interactions taking place between organisms in the field photographed on pages 12 and 13? Bacteria live in the soil of the field. Some bacteria even live inside the roots of some plants, including beans, peas, and soybeans. These bacteria help the plant by taking nitrogen from the air and converting it to a form that the plant needs in order to grow. Since all animals depend on plants for food, the interaction between these bacteria and plants is very important in all environments.

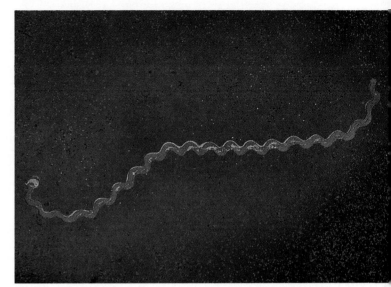

Leptospira, the bacteria that causes Weil's disease, is often spread by rats. Jaundice or meningitis may result from this bacteria.

Bacteria also feed on other living organisms. Sometimes when bacteria grow on living organisms, toxic chemicals the bacteria produce cause disease. Bacteria may also damage the tissues on which they are living. How many of the bacterial diseases listed in the chart on this page have you heard of?

Have you ever had a bacterial disease called strep throat? You caught it from someone, and you might have given it to someone, maybe your younger brother or sister or best friend. The bacteria that cause strep throat can be passed from one person to another. **Contagious** diseases are those that can be transmitted from one person to another.

In order for bacteria to cause disease, they must enter your body. Bacteria enter your body in a variety of ways. You can breathe them in through your nose. Bacteria can get on your hands and enter your body when you touch your eyes or mouth. They can enter your body when you eat contaminated food. They can also enter your body through a break in your skin.

When certain bacteria enter your blood or abdominal cavity, they may cause a serious infection. This environment is ideal for the growth

Bacterial Diseases in Humans

Disease	Area Affected
Strep Throat	Throat
Blood Poisoning	Entire Body
Whooping Cough	Respiratory Tract
Diphtheria	Respiratory Tract, Heart, and Kidneys
Tuberculosis	Lungs
Gonorrhea	Reproductive Organs

of these organisms. It is warm, moist, and full of nutrients. Infections can spread throughout your body and seriously interfere with its functioning. Why is the human body an ideal place for bacteria to grow?

Crown gall is a bacterial disease that causes tumors in plants.

Large numbers of bacteria that may not be harmful grow in parts of your body! Those that grow in your intestines even benefit you. Besides helping to digest food, certain bacteria in the intestines manufacture vitamin K, which is necessary for your good health. Many bacteria are present in your respiratory, urinary, and digestive tracts and on your skin all the time, and don't cause any problems.

Bacterial diseases affect plants, also. If a plant is damaged or weakened, it's easily infected by bacteria. The infections can affect all parts of a plant. When an infection becomes severe enough, the plant can't function properly. Some bacteria cause diseases like crown gall, characterized by tumor growth. Other bacteria cause diseases called wilts, where the flow of water or nutrients through the plant is blocked and portions of the plant wilt, or get limp, and die. Fire blight and leaf spots are diseases that cause dead, discolored areas on leaves, stems, or fruit. When these bacterial diseases affect crops like beans or pears, they can become very important for humans, also.

What other diseases do you know of that are caused by bacteria? How do they affect plants or animals? How do they affect you? Do the Literature Link on this page to investigate one bacterial disease that has had a tremendous impact on humans.

Literature Link

The Black Death

In 1347 the bubonic plague, or Black Death, a disease that was to devastate Europe, first appeared. It seemed that nothing could stop the spread of this deadly disease. No one knew the cause of the disease or a way to avoid contracting it.

Use *The Black Death* by James Day and other resources such as an encyclopedia to find out how the disease was spread and how it is treated today. Imagine you had this information when the plague began in 1347. What could you have advised the rulers of the time to do to prevent the spread of the disease? Write several paragraphs explaining your plan. Be sure to check your paragraphs for sense, spelling, and punctuation.

Cyanobacteria—
How Are They Different From Bacteria?

Monerans called bacteria get energy by breaking down food. **Cyanobacteria** (sī an′ ō bak tîr′ē ə) are monerans that make their own food through the process of photosynthesis. Recall that photosynthesis is the process plants use to produce food using energy from light. Because some cyanobacteria live in the ocean and have a pigment that colors them blue-green, for many years they were called blue-green algae and were classified as plants.

The classification was changed when scientists learned that the cell structure of cyanobacteria is more similar to bacteria than that of plants. Like bacteria, they don't have nuclei or organelles. They have cell walls, as plants do, but the cell walls of cyanobacteria are made of a different substance. Today these organisms are classified in the Kingdom Monera with bacteria.

Cyanobacteria are an important food source for many organisms because they produce food using the process of photosynthesis. The oxygen released by the process of photosynthesis is also used by other organisms in respiration. Cyanobacteria are not only beneficial, they are vital to other organisms in some environments.

Cyanobacteria growing on a pond

Besides the ocean, lakes, ponds, moist soils, swimming pools, and leaky faucets are common places for cyanobacteria to grow. They reproduce by fission and live as single cells, colonies, and long, threadlike chains. Many have a sticky capsule, like bacteria, that holds the cells together.

Cyanobacteria can sometimes have a harmful effect on their environment. Under certain conditions, cyanobacteria may grow rapidly and cover a body of water, such as a pond. This would happen when nutrients the cyanobacteria need for growth are abundant. Sewage dumped into a pond is a good source of nutrients. However, when that many cyanobacteria are present they can use up all the oxygen in the pond, and other organisms die from lack of oxygen. As these dead organisms decompose, they produce a foul odor. The green scum and smell are clues that the water can't be used for drinking!

Cyanobacteria in the ocean sometimes reproduce in such quantities that they form large mounds that we can easily see. These masses of cyanobacteria don't cause an oxygen shortage for other organisms in the vast ocean. They do, however, provide scientists with valuable information. These mounds or thick mats made of layers of cyanobacteria and sediments that form in warm, shallow seas are called stromatolites (strō mat′əl īts).

Stromatolites have existed during much of life's history on Earth. Fossilized stromatolites can be found in many parts of the world. Some stromatolites consist of fossilized cyanobacteria on the bottom, and living ones that are still being deposited on top. One of the most famous deposits is found in Shark Bay, Western Australia, where the mounds can be seen at the shoreline. Others are found in parts of Africa and the Bahamas. Many fossilized stromatolites are more than a meter in height, and some are more than three billion years in age! They date to a time when plants and animals as we know them had not yet evolved. Cyanobacteria evolved to carry on photosynthesis long before there were any plants. Scientists can study early cyanobacteria by observing fossilized stromatolites.

Stromatolites in a salt lagoon, Isla Angel de la Quarda, Baja, California

How Can Humans Control Bacteria?

Humans all over the world use bacteria to produce many foods, such as buttermilk. The milk products yogurt, cheese, cottage cheese, and sour cream are also produced by bacteria acting on milk. Different flavors of cheese are the result of different types of bacteria. Bacteria help to solidify cheese and yogurt. When allowed to grow in cucumbers or cabbage, bacteria turn them into pickles, kimchi, or sauerkraut. Vinegar is produced by bacteria growing in cider.

Bacteria in yogurt or buttermilk give those foods desirable qualities, but other bacteria can spoil food and make people ill. People have come up with many ways to keep bacteria from growing in their food. Do the Try This Activity below to investigate some of these methods.

TRY THIS

Can You Keep Bacteria From Growing in Food?

Bacteria fall from the air onto everything, including food. In this activity, you will investigate how additives can inhibit the growth of bacteria in food.

What You Need
bouillon broth
2 small spoons
20 mL white vinegar
salt
3 jars
masking tape
Activity Log page 8

Pour 50 mL of the prepared bouillon broth into each of three jars. To the first jar, add 1 spoonful of salt, and with a piece of tape, label it "salt." Add 1 spoonful of vinegar to a second jar and label it "vinegar." Add nothing to the third jar and label it "nothing." Place all the jars in a warm, dry place for 3 days. Record your observations in your *Activity Log*. Compare the appearance of the jars after 3 days. What conditions were held constant in the activity? What variable was tested? Which was the control? How do you explain the differences among the jars? How might salt or vinegar be used to preserve food?

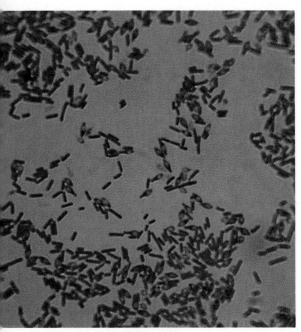

A type of anaerobic bacteria that produces endospores causes botulism.

When you did the Try This Activity on the previous page, did you observe that the salt or vinegar slowed down the growth of bacteria in food? Bacteria form vinegar by producing a chemical called an acid. However, acids will kill bacteria. As the acid builds up, even the bacteria that made the vinegar will be killed. Salt kills bacteria by removing water from the cells. Pickling food with vinegar, or salting foods, are methods people have used for many years to keep bacteria from growing on foods.

How long do you think the cans of food on the grocery store shelves have been there? Canned foods can be kept for years without spoiling. When the food is put into the cans, it's heated to a temperature hot enough to kill any bacteria that may be present. New bacteria can't enter because the can is sealed. However, some bacteria produce spores that can resist high heat. They may not be killed in the canning process.

Clostridium botulinum is a type of anaerobic bacteria that produces endospores that can withstand high heat. The inside of a can, where water and food but no oxygen are present, is a perfect environment for the spores to take in water and begin to reproduce. The carbon dioxide gas given off by anaerobic respiration will eventually cause the can to bulge. The toxin produced by this bacteria is deadly. The food poisoning known as botulism is produced by this toxin. If a can is bulging or damaged in some way, this is a sign that it is unsafe to consume its contents.

There are many methods of preserving food. A traditional method of preserving fish in Malaysia is by drying.

Have you ever read a milk carton and wondered what it means when it says the milk is pasteurized (pas′chə rīzd′)? Pasteurization is the process of heating milk to kill bacteria. Milk that has been pasteurized will spoil much more slowly. The buttermilk you used in the Explore Activity on pages 14 and 15 was pasteurized. The milk was then cultured. The kind of bacteria that would produce buttermilk was added to it.

Have you ever left a carton of milk out of the refrigerator for a long time? What was it like when you found it? Bacteria don't grow well in cold temperatures. Besides killing bacteria, humans prevent bacteria from growing by taking away one or more of the conditions that they need for survival and reproduction. Keeping food in a refrigerator is a way to inhibit the growth of bacteria. Freezing food lowers the temperature further, which inhibits the growth of bacteria even more. Food will last longer when it's frozen than it will when it's refrigerated.

Simply covering food will reduce bacterial growth. It won't prevent bacteria already on food from growing, but it will prevent new bacteria from landing on it. Cooking food and washing dishes at high temperatures are also ways to kill some bacteria.

Louis Pasteur, a 19th century French scientist, discovered that many diseases are caused by bacteria. He developed some methods to control bacteria that are still used today, including pasteurization, where food is heated to kill bacteria.

Some foods are dried because bacteria need water to grow. Pasta, like spaghetti, is an example. Pasta won't spoil for a long time at room temperature if it's kept dry. Vegetables such as tomatoes, or fruit such as apples can also be dried and won't spoil for a long time without refrigeration.

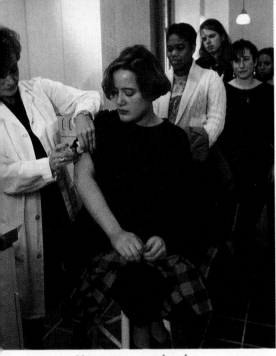

Have you received shots to protect you from the bacterial diseases whooping cough, diphtheria, or tetanus? The shots protect you against toxins the bacteria produce.

You can't use the same methods to keep bacteria off yourself that you use to keep them from growing in food. It wouldn't be healthy to sit in the refrigerator or put boiling water on yourself. You can wash yourself with soap and water to remove bacteria from your skin that might enter your body. Washing clothes will kill bacteria that grow on your clothes. You can brush your teeth to help remove bacteria from your mouth, or use fluoride toothpaste to make the tooth enamel stronger. If you cut yourself, putting an antiseptic on the cut will kill any bacteria that might be present. An antiseptic is a substance that will kill microorganisms on living tissue. Covering a cut will help keep bacteria out. Washing places where microorganisms may be found, such as sinks, toilets, or kitchen surfaces, with a disinfectant will kill bacteria that might infect you. A substance that kills microorganisms on objects is a disinfectant. What other good health habits prevent the spread of bacteria?

Minds On! In your *Activity Log* on page 9, list all of the products you can think of that are used in your home or school to kill harmful bacteria on or around people.●

Fortunately, your body is able to defend itself against many diseases, and there are medicines that help protect you. You have probably had shots to protect you against the bacterial diseases diphtheria, tetanus, and whooping cough. These shots actually protect you against poisons produced by these bacteria. If you are infected by bacteria, antibiotics —medicines that can kill bacteria or prevent them from reproducing—will help your body overcome the bacteria.

If you are interested in diseases caused by bacteria and how to prevent their spread, the book *Germs Make Me Sick!* has information on many diseases. See page 11 for more information.

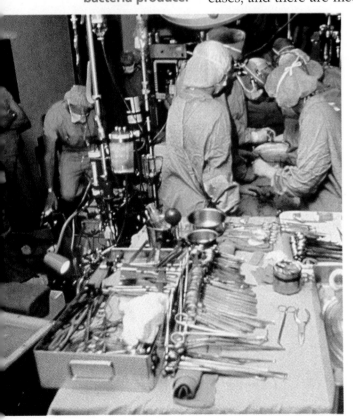

During surgery a person's body tissues are exposed to the air. Disease-causing bacteria can enter and cause a life-threatening infection. It's vital to keep operating rooms free from bacteria. Every surface in the room is cleaned with heat and disinfectants. Medical personnel clean their hands with antiseptics and wear protective clothing.

Sum It Up

Although at first glance monerans seem to be very simple, you now may view them as unique and productive. These one-celled organisms lacking a nucleus or organelles carry on the same life processes as more complex organisms.

Bacteria interact with other organisms by decomposing dead material in soil, sewage plants, or compost piles to release nutrients needed by living organisms. Decomposing bacteria in our intestines help our bodies function properly. Bacteria that interact with living organisms by feeding on them cause diseases, some with many consequences for humans. Since cyanobacteria undergo the process of photosynthesis, as plants do, they have a part in environments on Earth similar to plants—they are an important source of food and oxygen. Monerans can be both helpful and harmful to organisms they interact with, and many are necessary for life.

Using Vocabulary

bacteria   **microorganisms**
contagious   **monerans**
cyanobacteria

1. Imagine a new disease has been discovered. Write a paragraph or two about it using the vocabulary words *microorganisms, bacteria,* and *contagious,* and their correct definitions. You might want to describe the disease, tell what causes it, and explain how it can be prevented, as though you were writing a press release.

2. Imagine that NASA has explored a new planet circling a star in the Andromeda galaxy, and a one-celled organism that is similar to a cyanobacterium has been discovered. Describe it in a paragraph or two for a scientific journal by comparing it to cyanobacteria. Use the vocabulary words *monerans* and *cyanobacteria* correctly in the paragraph. You may also need to use the words *photosynthesis* or *producer* in your description.

Critical Thinking

1. What can happen in your body when you take too many antibiotics?

2. How do cyanobacteria contribute to pollution?

3. Botulism is a type of food poisoning caused by a toxin, or poison, produced by a kind of bacterium that produces endospores. Why do you think it's associated with canned foods and not fresh foods?

4. Suggest a reason why smoked meats don't spoil as quickly as fresh meats.

5. Which types of monerans might you find on the surface of damp soil? Three feet underground? In dry dust?

Protists—
Like Plants or Animals?

What does this whale have to do with simple organisms? Whales feed on simple organisms that live in ocean water, like those in the photographs on the next page.

How can one kingdom include organisms that resemble plants, others that resemble animals, and others that don't resemble either? These organisms are made of cells like those of plants and animals. They interact with other organisms by producing food as plants do or by consuming food as animals do, but they are much simpler than plants and animals.

Whales are among the world's largest animals. When they rise to the surface, huge waves of water roll aside. They can send great plumes of water many meters into the air with a flick of their tails. Did you ever wonder what a whale eats? Do you imagine it would take many fish to feed a hungry whale? Whales, like the one in the photograph on the previous page, don't eat fish or any large animals—they live on tiny animals, plants, and one-celled simple organisms living in ocean water—tons of them!

A world of microorganisms can be found in a drop of ocean water. Some of these, and similar organisms, can be found in a handful of damp soil, a ditch, or a drop of pond water. Some are found living inside plant or animal tissues, where they may cause disease. The White Cliffs of Dover, shown in the Introduction to this unit, were formed from the remains of simple organisms from this kingdom.

Minds On! The photos on the right show some of the organisms found in ocean water. The photo on the bottom right shows one simple organism that you'll read about in this lesson. What does it resemble? In your ***Activity Log*** on page 10, make a list of the ways this organism is similar to plants, animals, or bacteria.●

Since these organisms that live in ocean water are so small, microscopes are needed to see them. You'll have a chance to use a microscope to see the same type of simple organism in the next activity.

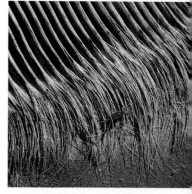

A baleen is used by whales to filter tiny organisms from ocean water as they swim.

13X

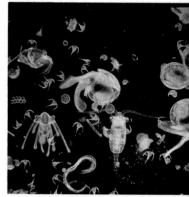

Whales feed on these tiny animals, plants, and simple organisms that live in the ocean in huge numbers.

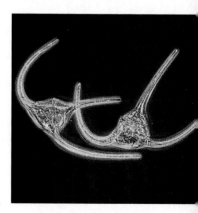

An important food source for the whale is a simple organism you will read about in this lesson.

Activity!

The World in a Drop of Water

You've seen some of the microscopic organisms found in a drop of ocean water. What do you think you'll find in a drop of pond water? A mud puddle? A fish tank?

What You Need

water from a pond, ditch, mud puddle, or fish tank
microscope
dropper
2 slides
2 coverslips
1 small cotton ball
***Activity Log* pages 11–12**

What To Do

Safety!

1 Put a drop of water from one of the water samples in the center of a clean slide. ***Safety Tip:*** Be careful with the glass slides. Avoid touching water samples with fingers, and wash hands when finished.

2 Put two fibers pulled from a cotton ball in the drop of water, and cover with a coverslip.

See the *Safety Tip* in step 1.

3 Observe the slide with the microscope on low power. When you find a microorganism, switch to high power and focus with the fine adjustment. Draw what you see in your *Activity Log*.

4 If you can locate a microorganism in the center of the slide, switch to high power. Focus with the fine adjustment. Draw the microorganism in your *Activity Log*. Include the color, shape, and any cell structures you see.

5 Repeat steps 3 and 4 for any microorganism you observe.

6 Repeat steps 1–5 using a different water sample.

What Happened?

1. What did the organisms you observed do when they bumped into a thread?
2. How did the microorganisms move?
3. What structures could you recognize inside the cells?
4. What characteristics did the organisms you observed have in common?
5. What characteristics were different?

What Now?

1. How are these organisms different from bacteria?
2. How do these organisms compare to plant or animal cells?

EXPLORE

309X

What Is a Protist?

How were the cells you observed in the Explore Activity alike? Did they remind you of bacteria, plants, or animals? You were observing single cells, like bacteria. Were there any cell parts inside the cells you observed? **Protists** (prō′ tists) are one-celled organisms with nuclei and organelles. Like bacteria, protists are one-celled organisms, but they have nuclei and organelles in their cytoplasm like plants and animals.

Were any of the protists you observed green? These protists are photosynthetic, producing food from energy in sunlight, as plants or cyanobacteria do. Other protists can't make their own food, but consume living or dead organisms for food, as animals or other simple organisms do.

What happened when a protist ran into the cotton fibers on the slide? What types of movement did you see, and could you tell what structures were producing the movement? Protists use flagella, cilia, or pseudopods to move. A **flagellum** (flə jel′ əm) is a long, whiplike structure that extends from a cell and propels the cell through water. **Cilia** (sil′ ē ə) are hairlike extensions of cells that can move. A **pseudopod** (sü′ də pod′) is an extension of the cytoplasm of a cell. Some protists are classified by these structures, and you'll read more about how protists move later in this lesson.

Two common protists

Protists have nuclei and organelles like plant and animal cells. Some protists have specialized structures called flagella and cilia projecting from them.

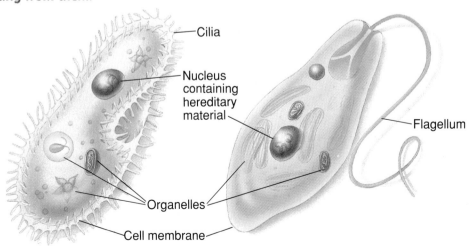

Cilia

Nucleus containing hereditary material

Flagellum

Organelles

Cell membrane

You've seen photographs of protists living in the ocean, and observed protists in fresh water from your own environment. Protists almost always live in water, or in moist environments, such as soil. Protists can be found almost anywhere on Earth where there is water, whether in the ocean or a mud puddle, that will dry up before the next rain.

In the Explore Activity on pages 34 and 35, you couldn't see the one-celled protists in the water samples without the use of a microscope. In the Math Link in Lesson 1, you calculated the size of a bacterium and a human cell seen through a microscope. You could calculate the size of a protist in the same way. Do the Math Link at the bottom of this page to explore magnification further.

Protists grow and reproduce in moist environments all around you. Most protists reproduce by mitosis, the same process of cell division that plant and animal cells undergo. The nucleus divides into two nuclei containing identical hereditary material. Then the cell divides into two equal-sized cells. Some protists reproduce by forming spores. You'll read more about spores in Lesson 3.

Math Link

Magnification—Drawing to Scale

When you observed the protists in the water sample with a microscope, you were looking at a magnified image. In the Math Link on page 17 in Lesson 1, you calculated the actual size of two cells seen through a microscope. Now you can explore the idea of magnification further. The protist shown below is magnified 100 times, as seen through a microscope. Inside the frame on page 13 of your *Activity Log,* draw a picture of the microorganism magnified only 50 times. Use a metric ruler and the grid over the frame to help you.

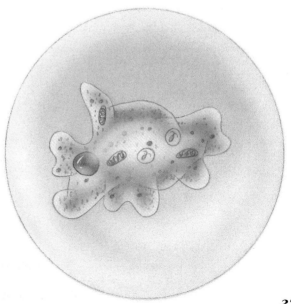

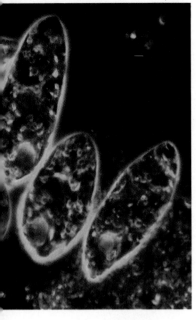

These protists contain chloroplasts.

Why Is It Called Protist?

The name *protist* means "first." Scientists have evidence that the first organism to evolve with a nucleus and organelles in its cytoplasm was very similar to a modern protist. Monerans were the first cells to live on Earth, and protists evolved from monerans. Can you speculate what organisms may have evolved from protists?

Scientists have been trying to explain how the organelles of protists could have evolved from monerans since the last century. During the 1960s Dr. Lynn Margulis, a biologist who taught at Boston University, built on a theory formed by Russian biologists at the turn of the century. She hypothesized that organelles like chloroplasts, the ones that carry on the process of photosynthesis in many cells, actually evolved from cells like monerans.

What would happen if you put a cyanobacterium into an animal cell? What could the cyanobacterium do that the animal cell could not? Dr. Margulis hypothesized that a billion years or more ago, moneran cells similar to cyanobacteria invaded larger cells that couldn't make their own food. Instead of one or both being killed, the cyanobacteria and larger cells both benefited from the relationship. The cyanobacteria produced food by photosynthesis. The larger cells used the food, and the cyanobacteria were protected by being inside the larger cells. Over millions of years, the two kinds of organisms evolved to become one.

After studying the traits of cell structures found in plant and animal cells, most scientists are convinced that Dr. Margulis' hypothesis is correct. The cells of protists, as well as all plant and animal cells, trace their ancestry back to relationships that may have developed nearly a billion years ago.

Dr. Lynn Margulis developed a theory that protists evolved from monerans. This research also helps scientists understand the evolution of plants and animals.

269X

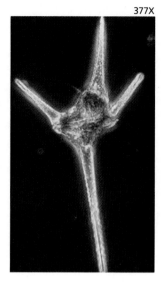

377X

What characteristics could these protists have in common with plants?

Plantlike Protists

The plantlike protists resulting from the evolution of cyanobacteria and other cells exist in a variety of forms, some encased in shells, others possessing structures called flagella or cilia that enable them to move. Many of them have pigments that give them various colors, although they all contain the green pigment chlorophyll as plants do. How would it be beneficial for a plantlike organism to be able to move? Do the Try This Activity on this page to find out.

TRY THIS

Activity!

How Do Protists Respond to Light?

Some protists have the ability to move, others don't. What is the advantage of the ability to move? You can form a hypothesis about how one protist will respond to light and then test your hypothesis.

What You Need

slide, dropper, live *Euglena* culture, coverslip, microscope, index card, *Activity Log* page 14

Safety Tip: Be careful with glass slides and coverslips. With a dropper, place 1 drop of *Euglena* (ū glē′ nə)

culture within the circle. Place a coverslip on the slide. Observe the slide with the microscope under low power. When you find *Euglena,* describe its structure in your *Activity Log.* Place the index card under the right half of the slide, so the light source is cut off for half the slide. Formulate a hypothesis about how *Euglena* will respond to light, based on what you have seen of its structure. Write your hypothesis in your *Activity Log.* After 2 min, remove the card. Make three observations at each side of the slide, counting the number of organisms each time. Average the three numbers for each side. Where are most of the *Euglena?* Record your observations and explain the results. Was your hypothesis confirmed or not? Why did *Euglena* respond as it did? What advantage does it give this protist to be able to move? *Safety Tip:* Wash your hands when you are finished disposing of the slides.

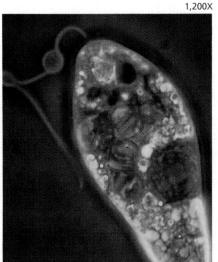

1,200X

Euglenoids

Plantlike protists may be divided into many groups, three of which are very important to humans. Euglenoids (ū glē′ nöidz′) make up one group. The *Euglena* you observed in the last activity belong in this group. These one-celled green organisms are common in fresh water, such as ponds and lakes, but not in the ocean. Did you observe that the *Euglena* moved toward the light in the activity? These organisms move with a flagellum.

Did you notice a spot-like structure in *Euglena?* This structure, called a stigma or "eyespot," contains a material that is sensitive to light. The eyespot is shaded from light on a few sides so that it can receive light from only one direction. This allows the organism to "sense" the direction of a light source. The eyespot responds to light, and the flagellum moves the organism toward the light. The ability to locate light and move toward it helps the organism make food.

Euglenoid

Dinoflagellates

Dinoflagellates (dī nō flaj′ ə lāts) are plantlike protists that live mostly in the ocean where they form part of plankton, the microscopic food that whales and other marine animals live on. They have two flagella that are at a right angle to each other. Many dinoflagellates have stiff plates inside their cells that give the appearance of shells.

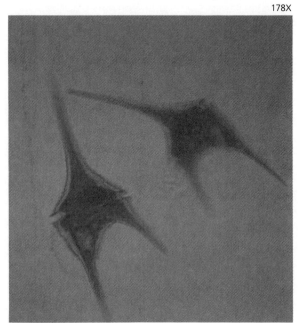

178X

Have you ever heard of a *red tide?* Many dinoflagellates produce toxins that can kill marine animals—or humans. Some species of dinoflagellates, which contain red pigments, will reproduce until there is a huge mass floating in the ocean. This mass, or red tide, is poisonous, and people who fish know to avoid catching anything that might have been contaminated by the toxins released by this protist.

Dinoflagellates also possess a peculiar and beautiful trait. Have you ever heard of lights appearing in the ocean on the crests of waves at night? Like fireflies, many dinoflagellates release light through a process known as **bioluminescence** (bī ō lü mən nes sənts). The dinoflagellates break down certain energy-containing substances in their cells, and light is released in the process.

Dinoflagellates

Diatoms

Diatoms (dī'ə tomz) are a group of plantlike protists that form hard shells around themselves. Huge numbers of these protists live in fresh and salt water. They provide most of the oxygen in Earth's atmosphere as a by-product of photosynthesis. Diatoms are also the major food source for animals such as whales. Some of the animals in the ocean that rely on diatoms and other protists for food are, in turn, a food source for other animals. Directly or indirectly, these protists are a vital source of energy for organisms on Earth.

Diatom

Animal-like Protists—Protozoans

A **protozoan** (prō' tə zō'ən) is a protist with some of the characteristics of animals. Animal-like protists consume plants or other organisms for food. Scientists once classified these protists as part of the animal kingdom. They were called protozoa, meaning "first animals." Today, protozoa is the name of the group in the Kingdom Protista where these organisms are classified. Protozoans can be distinguished from each other by their movement. Do the Try This Activity on this page to explore one kind of animal-like protists.

TRY THIS

Activity!

What Are Cilia Used For?

Protists that consume food instead of producing it are classified by whether or not they move, and how they move. As you observe several similar protozoans, notice how they are moving, and think about why they need to move.

What You Need

live *Paramecium* and *Stentor* cultures, 2 droppers, 2 slides, 2 coverslips, microscope, *Activity Log* page 15

Safety Tip: Be careful with glass slides and coverslips. Using a dropper, place a small drop of *Paramecium* (par' ə mē'se əm) on a slide, and cover with a coverslip. Examine the organisms with the microscope under low power. Record your observations in your *Activity Log,* including any motion you see. Make a slide of *Stentor* (sten'tôr) using the same procedure, and observe these organisms. Record your observations in your *Activity Log.* What do these organisms have in common with each other? Why do they need to move? *Safety Tip:* Wash your hands after disposing of the slides.

Ciliates

Paramecium and *Stentor,* which you observed in the Try This Activity on the previous page, both have cilia protruding from their cell membranes. Protozoans that have cilia are classified together.

The constant beating of cilia moves these organisms through water. For example, by controlling the movements of its cilia, *Paramecium* can stop suddenly, rotate like a spinning football, or go backwards. Did you observe any of these movements? Since these protists consume food, as animals do, their ability to move helps them find food.

Cilia also help these organisms take in food once it has been located. For example, you may have seen *Paramecium* consuming food in the water sample you observed in the Explore Activity on pages 34 and 35. Food particles, such as bacteria and organic matter in the water, are swept by cilia toward a groove in *Paramecium*. There they form sacks around food particles and carry them into the cell for digestion.

Stentor—a type of ciliate

270X

What characteristics could these protists have in common with animals?

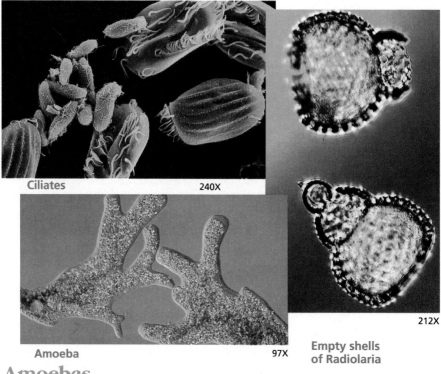

Ciliates   240X

Amoeba   97X

Empty shells of Radiolaria

212X

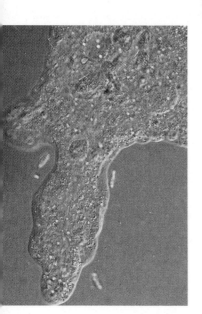

A pseudopod extending from a freshwater amoeba

Amoebas

One kind of animal-like protists, called amoebas (ə mē′bəs), move by forming "false feet," or pseudopods. The amoeba pulls or pushes itself over a surface by extending a pseudopod and then pulling the rest of the cell after it. Pseudopods are also used for feeding. The illustration on the next page describes this process.

Amoebas surround a particle of food or another organism with a pseudopod. The cell membrane forms a sack around the food, and this sack moves inside the cell. The food is then digested inside the cell.

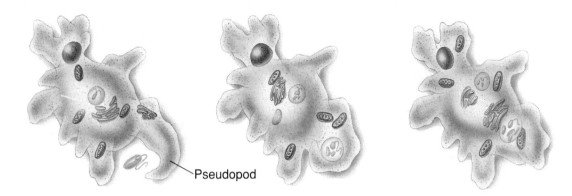

Pseudopod

Some amoebas form shells around their cells. *Foraminifera* (fə ram ə nif′ ə rə) are amoebas, and they formed the microscopic snail-like shells that are found in the White Cliffs of Dover. You saw those shells on page 7 of this unit.

Flagellates

Protozoans that have flagella are called flagellates. These organisms can move by whipping one or more flagella back and forth. Most flagellates live in and feed on living animals. Some live in living organisms without causing harm. For example, certain flagellates live inside the digestive tract of termites. Some termites build and live in huge mounds of soil on the African savannah. Others "eat" the wood in floorboards and frames of houses, causing great damage. Termites actually can't eat wood. Some have flagellates inside their intestines that digest wood and secrete a waste chemical that feeds the termites.

Minds On! Termites and protists live together as a team. Neither one can survive without the other. Can you think of any other relationships between organisms where neither one can survive without the other? Discuss your ideas with your classmates, and write your ideas in your ***Activity Log*** on page 16.●

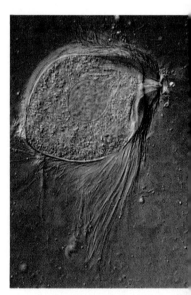

A flagellate lives in termite intestines.

Sporozoans

The last kind of protozoans, called sporozoans (spôr′ə zō′ənz), depends on other organisms to live. They form a type of reproductive cell called a spore. Sporozoans resemble amoebas but none of them can move. These protozoans live inside other living organisms and feed on them. Often the sporozoans will only live in specific organisms or only in parts of an organism. Many of these protozoans cause serious diseases.

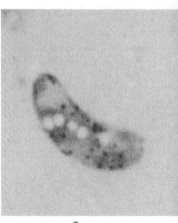

Sporozoan

Slime Molds—Not Like Plants or Animals

Plasmodial slime mold

36X

Organisms called slime molds are also classified in the Kingdom Protista, but in a separate group from the plantlike protists and protozoans. Although they have characteristics in common with protozoans, they also have characteristics in common with fungi, which are organisms you'll discover in Lesson 3.

Slime molds consume food by engulfing bacteria, fungi, or decayed particles in soil. They live in the decayed layer of leaf litter in forests, in moist soil, or on rotting tree stumps. Slime molds use pseudopods to move, as amoebas do. They also produce the reproductive cells called spores.

Although slime molds are one-celled, they form complex structures that produce spores. Some slime molds look like what you would expect—brightly colored slime that spreads out in a net of fine strands. Although these slime molds are easily visible, they are actually huge single cells. The reproductive structure forms from the single cell. At some stage in their life cycle, slime molds resemble amoebas. At certain times, they group together and form a spore-producing structure that looks like a multicellular organism.

37X

A cellular slime mold

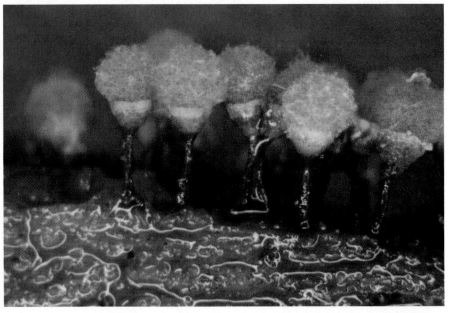

The structures will produce reproductive cells called spores. A one-celled organism produced these structures!

44

Disease-causing Interactions

Many protists cause disease in animals. Certain amoebas cause dysentery, a severe type of diarrhea. People often acquire dysentery from drinking water in which the amoebas are living. A flagellate called *Trypanosoma* (tri pan′e sōmə) causes sleeping sickness when it lives in human blood. *Trypanosoma* is carried by an insect called the tsetse (tēt′ sē) fly. These protists multiply in the blood until they may be as numerous as blood cells. Without treatment, death usually results.

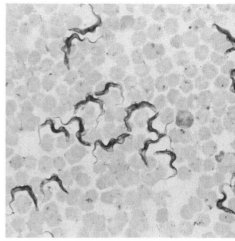

690X

The flagellates that cause sleeping sickness, in blood

The sporozoan *Plasmodium* (plaz mō′dē əm) lives in the blood of people and causes the disease malaria. If you've ever lived in tropical South America, Asia, or Africa, you may have had malaria, or know someone who did. Although it can be successfully treated, malaria is still a serious disease affecting millions of people in these regions. The symptoms of malaria include a high fever alternating with sweating and chills.

People are infected with plasmodia through the bite of a female anopheles mosquito. The mosquito bites the skin and sucks a person's blood. If the mosquito is infected with plasmodia, the protists can enter the person's bloodstream. Plasmodia reproduce inside the red blood cells, eventually bursting these cells. Each time red blood cells are destroyed, they release substances that cause the person to be sick. The blood is also less able to carry oxygen because of the destruction of red blood cells. This condition is called anemia. Infected cells are carried to the liver by the blood, where the plasmodia infect liver cells.

Fighting malaria has often meant eliminating the mosquito that carries it. This has been done through the use of insecticides. What drawbacks are there to using insecticides? Swamps where the mosquitoes breed have been drained to prevent the mosquito population from growing. What other steps could be taken to fight malaria?

Minds On! You are going on a trip to central Africa. What precautions will you take to avoid catching malaria? Make a list in your ***Activity Log*** on page 17.●

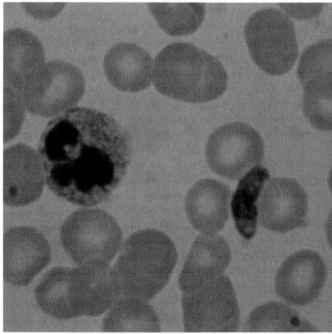

2,050X

The plasmodia that cause malaria, in blood

One of the areas where malaria is common is central Africa. In some areas there are many standing bodies of water, such as irrigation canals or puddles, where mosquitoes breed. This leads to frequent outbreaks of malaria. In these areas, a disease called sickle cell anemia is also common. Why do these diseases exist side by side?

Sickle cell anemia is found among Americans of African or Mediterranean descent. This disease is inherited when both parents pass on hereditary material that affects red blood cells. The red blood cells of people who have sickle cell anemia break easily. They also become misshapen and clog small blood vessels causing severe pain in parts of the body. There are few treatments for sickle cell anemia at this time. Although some people with this disease can live into middle age, many affected people don't live past their teens.

An important fact about sickle cell anemia is that a person can have the different type of red blood cells without becoming sick. The disease will develop only if the red blood cells are severely affected. This happens only when both parents of a person had this type of red blood cell. In parts of Africa near the equator, where malaria is very common, many Africans have the different type of red blood cell, because it is a good defense mechanism. Although the disease sickle cell anemia is very serious, having the different type of red blood cells helps people resist malaria.

If such a person is infected with a plasmodium by a mosquito, the plasmodium can't grow properly inside the different red blood cells. As a result, the person may not become sick. Although having different red blood cells is beneficial for people living in regions where malaria is common, the trait does not benefit people now living in the United States, where malaria is rare.

Dr. Roland Scott, a pediatrician and expert on sickle cell anemia, began studying the disease in the 1940s. He founded the Howard University Center for Sickle Cell Anemia.

These maps of Asia and Africa show the distribution of malaria and sickle cell anemia.

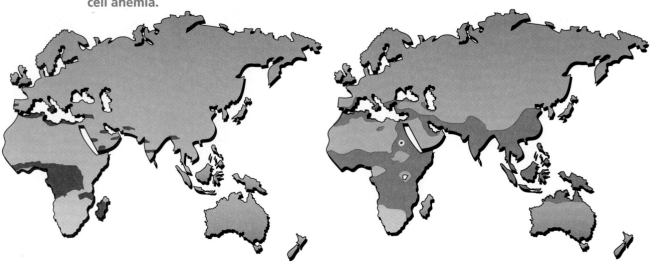

What Can Protists Do for Humans?

Minds On! Resourceful humans have used simple organisms in many ways. How could protists be useful to us? In your *Activity Log* on page 18, list several uses you can imagine for protists based on what you know about them.●

Now do the Try This Activity on this page to learn about a wonderful, multipurpose, all-natural substance provided by protists.

TRY THIS

Activity!

Animal, Vegetable, or Mineral?

Does the name *diatomaceous* (dī ət ə mā′ shəs) *earth* sound familiar? Observe some under a microscope to see why.

What You Need

diatomaceous earth, slide, coverslip, microscope, dropper, water, *Activity Log* page 19

Take a pinch of diatomaceous earth between your fingers and rub them together. Describe the texture of it in your *Activity Log*. Put a very small amount of diatomaceous earth on a glass slide and spread it out to make a thin layer. *Safety Tip:* Be careful with glass slides and coverslips. Describe the appearance of it. Add 2 drops of water to your sample. Add a coverslip and observe it under low and high power. Describe and draw what you see in your *Activity Log*. Based on your observations, do you think diatomaceous earth was ever alive? Explain why or why not. How do you think this substance was formed? What do you think diatomaceous earth could be used for?

The diatomaceous earth you saw in the Try This Activity above contains the shells of diatoms, the protist described earlier that is an important food source for many ocean animals. Diatoms form thin, glass-like shells over their cell membranes, in a great variety of shapes. Although diatomaceous earth resembles sand, the diatom shells seen under a microscope don't look like grains of sand.

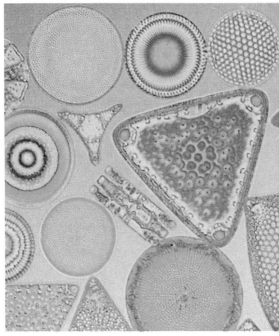

These fossilized diatom shells were formed millions of years ago and fell to an ancient ocean floor.

310X

The diatomaceous earth you observed in the Try This Activity on the previous page began forming millions of years ago when the shells of diatoms that died sank to the ocean floor. In time, the ocean floor rose in some places and became dry land. Deposits of diatom shells that have piled up for millions of years still exist in places.

The shells contain a substance called silica that has special properties that are useful to us. Each shell is almost like a small bit of broken glass. This makes diatomaceous earth hard and rough. Because of this, it's a good abrasive in some polishes and toothpastes. Diatomaceous earth is also used in aquarium filters, swimming pool filters, and as a pesticide in gardens, where the rough shell pieces are spread on plants to irritate or kill slugs and insects that crawl on them.

Since diatomaceous earth is made of the remains of organisms, what do you think will happen to it when it's washed into the soil or thrown into a landfill? What would happen to a filter, abrasive, or pesticide made from chemicals under the same circumstances? Some chemicals are toxic to living organisms. Some don't break down easily and may remain in soil or water for a long time.

Minds On! Will diatomaceous earth deposits ever run out? How could we get more? Do you think it's more or less expensive than a chemical pesticide? Which do you think would be the best pesticide? Make a list of pros and cons about using diatomaceous earth as a pesticide versus chemicals, and write it on page 20 in your *Activity Log.*●

The shells of diatoms, such as these, are a major component of diatomaceous earth.

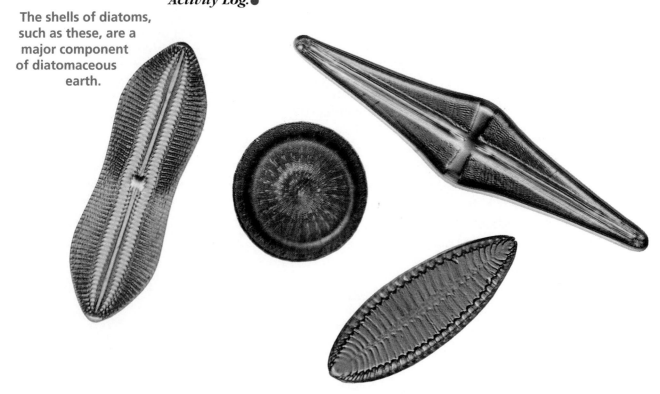

48

Sum It Up

Protists are one-celled organisms, like monerans, but have nuclei and organelles in their cytoplasm, like plants and animals. Many protists are able to move by using flagella, cilia, or pseudopods. Being able to move enables protists to find food, react to light, or take in food. Diatoms, dinoflagellates, and euglenoids interact with other organisms the way plants do. They are a vital food source for other organisms, and produce much of the oxygen in Earth's atmosphere. Protozoans and slime molds interact with organisms the way animals do—they consume other organisms. Protists that feed on living organisms can cause disease in plants and animals. These diseases sometimes have a tremendous impact on humans.

Using Vocabulary

bioluminescence
cilia
flagellum
protists
protozoan
pseudopod

Pretend you are a protozoan. Write several paragraphs describing your life in a drop of water. Use all the vocabulary words correctly. Consider describing your own cell, or those organisms you observe around you. How will you interact with them?

Critical Thinking

1. Which protozoans are the least animal-like? Explain your answer.
2. How else might flagella benefit euglenas besides enabling them to find food?
3. What would happen if all protists in the oceans disappeared?
4. Explain why animal-like protists are not classified in the animal kingdom.
5. If you had never seen a protist cell, or measured one, what do you know about protists that would lead you to speculate that protists are bigger than monerans?

Fungi- Not-So-Simple Organisms

A tree is part of a forest environment. Both alive and dead, it interacts with other organisms and the physical environment in the forest. The photographs on the next page give a closer look at the organism growing on the tree. What is its part in the forest?

What grows in the soil that is neither plant nor animal, and cannot produce its own food? In this lesson, you will study organisms that interact with dead or living organisms by secreting chemicals that digest them, then absorbing them as food.

What interaction is taking place between the tree and the simple organism growing on it in the photograph on the opposite page? What is the simple organism eating? Where have you seen organisms like this one before, and what were they living on?

If you've ever left a glass of milk out of the refrigerator accidentally and observed fuzzy growths on it later, or picked up an orange and found it soft and covered with green fuzz, you've seen some organisms that are related to the organism growing on the tree. When you saw these growths, did you throw the food away immediately?

Imagine smelling a freshly baked pizza. Mushrooms are the same type of simple organism as the fuzzy growth on decomposing food and the organism on the tree. What if you left the mushrooms off the pizza? You would still need simple organisms related to mushrooms to make the crust and cheese.

Minds On! Where else do these simple organisms grow, and how else do we use them? In your *Activity Log* on page 21, list places where you think organisms like the mushroom or fuzzy growths can be found in your home or school. Look back at the list. What characteristics do these places have in common? What were the simple organisms doing there?●

You probably never thought much about these simple organisms when you saw them—or perhaps you tried not to think of them. These interesting organisms are found everywhere, and although sometimes they are unwanted, they contribute greatly to our lives. It's hard to imagine life without them. As you perform the next Explore Activity, you will learn more about these simple organisms.

The simple organism growing on the birch tree has an important function in the forest.

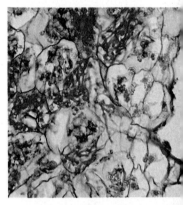

Looking more closely, can you tell how a tree and an organism like this one interact?

This part of the simple organism extends into the tree.

Activity!

What Makes a Fungus a Fungus?

What do the diverse organisms mentioned on pages 50 and 51 have in common? As you observe the mushroom in this activity, look for structures that are not typical of plants or animals.

What You Need

goggles
2 droppers
water
slide
fresh whole mushroom
forceps
coverslip
microscope
iodine
paper towel
Activity Log pages 22–23

What To Do

1 *Safety Tip:* Wear goggles to perform this activity. Prepare a slide by placing a drop of water on it.
Safety Tip: Be careful with glass slide and coverslip.

2 Observe the structure of the mushroom and draw it in your *Activity Log*.

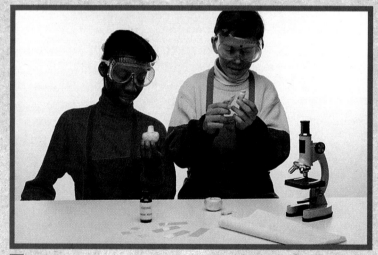

3 Break the stalk of the mushroom off the cap. Using the forceps, peel a small piece off the stalk to expose the inside of the stalk. Using the forceps, peel a thin piece from the inside of the stalk, peeling down the stalk (not across).

4 Place the thin piece of mushroom stalk in the drop of water. Make sure it is flat, then place a coverslip on it.

Safety!

See the *Safety Tips* in steps 1 and 6.

5 Observe the slide using the microscope on low power, then high power. Describe and draw what you see in your *Activity Log*.

6 Using the second dropper, place a drop of iodine at the edge of the coverslip. Place the edge of the paper towel at the opposite edge of the coverslip. The iodine will be pulled across the slide. *Safety Tip:* Iodine stains. Do not spill on your clothes, skin, or table.

7 Observe the stained slide using the microscope on low and high power. Describe and draw what you see in your *Activity Log*.

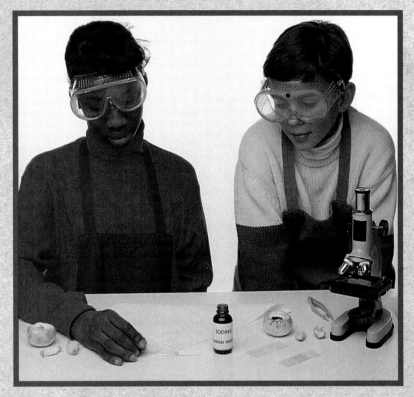

What Happened?

1. Did the mushroom have any roots, leaves, or flowering structures?
2. How did the structure of the mushroom compare to bacteria? To protists?
3. What structures did you observe that were different from organisms you have seen before?

What Now?

1. How do you think the mushroom was acquiring nutrients to survive and grow?
2. On your previous illustration of the mushroom in your *Activity Log*, label the structure you think is used in acquiring food.

What Is a Fungus?

What do mushrooms and other fungi have in common? At first the answer may not seem obvious. From observing the mushroom in the Explore Activity on pages 52 and 53, you probably concluded that it didn't look much like mold—the fuzzy mounds that grow in decomposing food. Neither a package of powdery yeast nor the mildew that grows in some showers looks much like either the mold or the mushroom. Once you observed the cells of the mushroom and the way they were organized, how did it compare to other organisms you know about?

A mushroom is a type of fungus. **Fungi** (fun'jī) are simple organisms made of cells that have cell walls and absorb food from their surroundings. The cells of the mushroom have nuclei and organelles like plants, animals, and protists. The cells of the mushroom have cell walls, as plants do, although the cell wall is made of a different material. Most fungi consist of many cells organized into structures, as plants and animals are, although the structures are much simpler. There were no roots, leaves, or skin in the fungus you observed.

The cells of a fungus form thin, winding, branching filaments called hyphae (hī' fē). Hyphae are made of many cells with pores between them. The illustration on this page shows how the cells in hyphae are connected, so the cytoplasm can flow back and forth. The cap and stalk of a mushroom are made of tightly packed hyphae. There is another part to a mushroom that you didn't observe. This part remains underground, beneath the stalk and cap. Here, the hyphae wind together to form a mesh called a mycelium (mī sē' lē ə m).

Fungi are made of hyphae, formed of many cells with pores between them. Hyphae make up a mycelium.

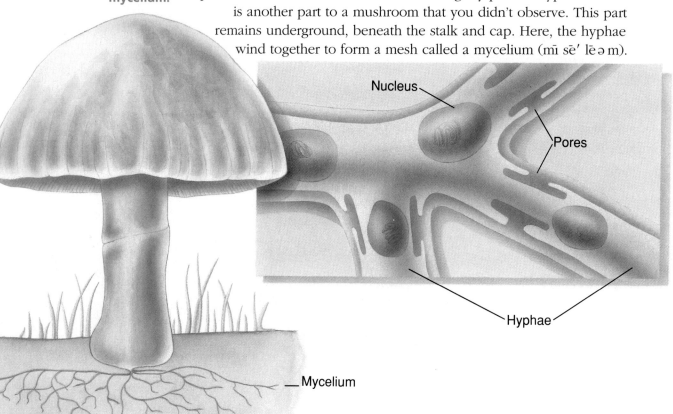

Nucleus

Pores

Hyphae

Mycelium

54

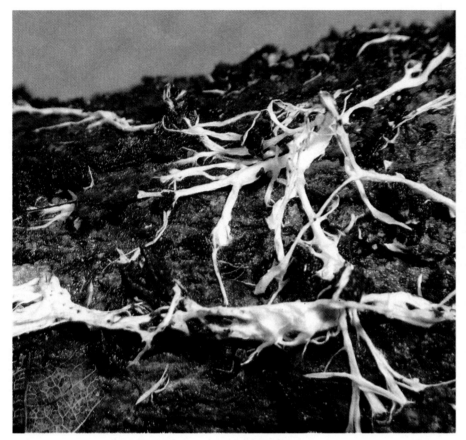

The mycelium of a mushroom grows underground.

Mushroom

A mold growing on a strawberry

Where do mushrooms grow naturally? What do they use for food? Fungi, like plants, are made of many cells containing nuclei, and many types of fungi grow in soil, but fungi do not produce food by the process of photosynthesis. They are consumers, but don't eat the way animals do. They digest their food source by secreting chemicals onto it from their hyphae. The food source is broken down into nutrients by the chemicals, and the nutrients are absorbed by the hyphae.

Organisms in the Kingdom Fungi can be placed into four groups. You have observed an organism from one group—mushrooms. The fungi that cause the diseases rusts and smuts are grouped with mushrooms. Molds are grouped together, and yeasts make up a third group. Fungi that cause diseases such as Chestnut blight and Dutch elm disease are also related to yeasts. The fourth group, water molds and mildews, are fungi that are most often one-celled, although some may be highly branched, multicellular strands. Water molds and mildews live in fresh water or moist soil, where they feed on the remains of dead organisms. Unfortunately, they also feed on many living plants that are important to humans.

Yeast

A water mold growing on a tomato

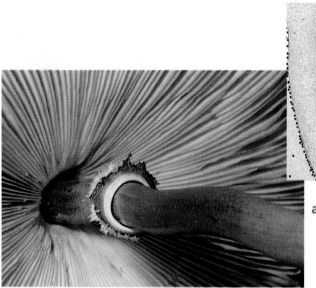

Gills

Spore-producing structure

Underneath the mushroom cap are gills. A closer look at the gills reveals spore-producing structures lining them.

What did the underside of the mushroom cap you observed in the Explore Activity on pages 52 and 53 look like? Did you notice structures resembling gills? The gills of a mushroom contain microscopic reproductive structures. These black structures are spore cases that hold thousands of microscopic spores. The illustration and photographs on this page show the spore-producing structures of a mushroom. **Spores** are cells from which new organisms are produced without being fertilized by another cell.

When the spore cases break open, thousands of spores are released into the air. These light spores are easily carried by currents of air, by water, or by animals that brush against a fungus. Some spores are brightly colored, which gives molds their color.

Many people are allergic to spores. The sneezing, red eyes, and runny noses, often occurring in the spring and fall, result from allergies to spores released by millions of fungi.

When a spore lands on an object and there is adequate moisture and warmth, it reproduces and grows into a new fungus. This asexual reproduction produces a fungus that is identical to the fungus that produced the spore.

Fungi also reproduce by sexual reproduction. Two fungi can produce sex cells that unite to form a single cell, which then multiplies to form a new fungus. The new fungus will be different from the fungi that produced it, because two organisms combined their hereditary material. The illustration on the next page shows the life cycle of a bread mold, including both sexual and asexual reproduction.

Where have you seen fungi growing in your home or neighborhood? To reproduce, fungi need moisture. They grow better in darkness than in light. Fungi don't need light for photosynthesis, as plants do, because they can't make their own food.

How do mushrooms interact with their environment?

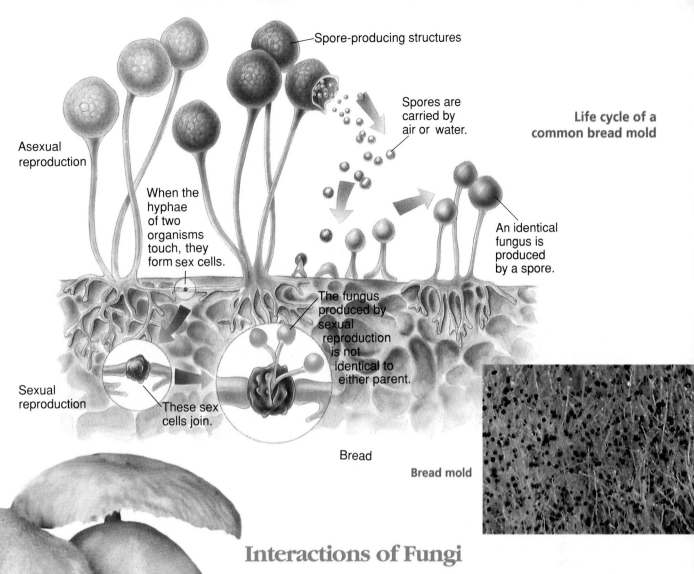

Spore-producing structures

Spores are carried by air or water.

Life cycle of a common bread mold

Asexual reproduction

When the hyphae of two organisms touch, they form sex cells.

An identical fungus is produced by a spore.

The fungus produced by sexual reproduction is not identical to either parent.

Sexual reproduction

These sex cells join.

Bread

Bread mold

Interactions of Fungi

How do mushrooms grow in soil without roots? Fungi anchor themselves by extending hyphae into the surface where they are growing. The hyphae release chemicals that break down dead organic material into nutrients. The hyphae then absorb the nutrients and water from the surroundings. In this manner, fungi get food by digesting dead organisms. The fungus growing on the tree in the photograph on page 50 was digesting the tree bark. The mushrooms on the rotting log in the photograph on the previous page are breaking down the dead log. The mold that grows on old food digests it and absorbs its nutrients.

The interactions of fungi that decompose dead organisms are beneficial to the environment. The millions of microscopic fungi that live in a handful of soil break down organic matter into nutrients that can be used by living organisms. Decomposing prevents dead organisms, like the fallen log, from piling up. Unfortunately, fungi also decompose materials such as cloth, paper, and even rubber. Fungi often cause problems for humans by decomposing books or clothing that get damp.

57

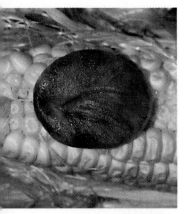

Corn smut is a fungal disease.

Some fungi grow in living organisms. Hyphae absorb nutrients from the living tissue. These fungi may cause disease or kill the organisms they're living in. The white growth that is common on fish is a water mold. In humans, ringworm and athlete's foot are caused by fungi that infect the skin. Thrush is a fungal disease that affects the mouth and is common in infants.

This interaction between a fungus and another organism is also a problem for humans when a fungus attacks crops, trees, or garden plants. For example, smuts and rusts are fungal diseases that attack corn, wheat, rye, barley, oats, and wild grasses.

Some water molds and mildews cause disease by attacking crops as diverse as grapes, tomatoes, soybeans, or rubber plants. In 1846 and 1847, the entire potato crop of Ireland became infected with a water mold that spreads through damp soil. There was no treatment for the disease. Farmers watched helplessly as their potatoes were turned soggy and black by the water mold.

Potatoes were a major source of income in Ireland, not to mention food! More than 800,000 people starved to death in the famine that resulted. Thousands of others left Ireland to come to the United States in search of work when their crops were destroyed. The population of Ireland dropped by 50 percent in ten years because of death and people moving away.

Minds On! Do you think the disease that infected Ireland's potato crop changed the course of history? What effects do you think there were on Ireland in the years after the disease passed? Discuss your ideas with your classmates, and write them in your *Activity Log* on page 24.●

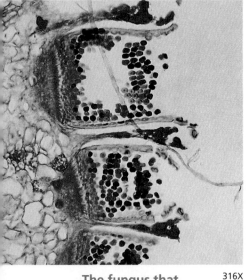

316X

The fungus that causes wheat rust grows in the plant tissues.

Water molds commonly infect fish.

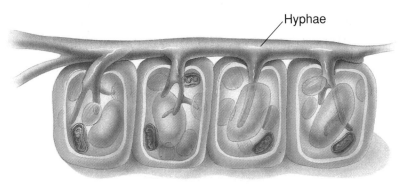

Hyphae

Plant cells

Fungi grow into the tissues of plants they infect. This illustration shows how the hyphae of a water mold grow into the leaf of a potato plant.

If you are interested in this topic, *The Potato Eaters* is a good book about one Irish family that is affected by the potato famine, and moves to America. See the Science in Literature bibliography on page 11 for further information.

Fungi that infect plants may kill them by destroying the plant tissue. They may damage or kill plants in other ways, also. Certain molds that grow on plants produce powerful poisons. These molds affect not only the plant, but the animals that eat the plants. The Health Link on this page describes the effect of one toxic fungus on humans.

Health Link

St. Anthony's Fire

During the Middle Ages and even into modern times, people living in agricultural societies who grew a grain called rye sometimes became very ill. The illness, called ergotism (ər′gət iz′ əm), caused people to have severe muscle spasms, poor blood circulation, difficulty breathing, and even resulted in hallucinations and some forms of mental illness. In parts of Europe, the disease was known as St. Anthony's fire. Because the cause of the disease was unknown and there was no treatment, many people died from the disease.

Today doctors know that ergotism is caused by toxins. The toxins are produced by a fungus called ergot that infects rye grain. The fungus grows in the rye seeds. Long purple structures form among the seeds and stick out. These form structures that produce spores. The toxins enter the body of a person who eats rye infected with the fungus, and affect the nervous system.

The dark structures in this head of rye grain are parts of a fungus called ergot.

Although ergot still infects rye, it's rare. Farmers use many methods to control the spread of the fungus. They rotate crops, take care to plant seeds that aren't infected, and destroy infected grain. The disease ergotism doesn't occur today because rye grain is cleaned before it's made into flour and baked goods.

Although this fungus has had serious effects on humans, ergot has also been of benefit to humans. Scientists have analyzed the compounds contained in the toxin. Some of their effects have been put to good use by humans. The toxin produced by ergot stops bleeding. Do some library research or interview a doctor or nurse to discover what this substance is used for today.

Where would a farmer use fungicides to kill fungi?

Most crop plants are susceptible to various kinds of fungi. Each year in the United States, hundreds of millions of dollars are lost as a result of crop damage caused by fungi. Farmers apply special fungicides to their crops to kill fungi and to prevent their growth. Fungicides are mixed with soil to prevent fungi from growing on plant roots and are added to stored grain in silos.

Another way of protecting crops from fungi is to breed plants that are resistant to a specific fungus. Various varieties of wheat, for example, resist fungal diseases.

Some fungi have developed a unique way of absorbing food without harming an organism they are using as a food source. Do the Try This Activity below to explore these organisms.

TRY THIS

Activity!

A Fungus Interacting

What do the organisms called lichens (lī′kənz) have to do with fungi? By observing the structure of a lichen, you can infer another relationship between fungi and other organisms, and operationally define a lichen.

What You Need

lichen, forceps, slide, coverslip, dropper, water, microscope, *Activity Log* page 25

Observe the lichen and record its appearance in your *Activity Log*. Place a drop of water on the slide. Using the forceps, remove a small piece of lichen from the sample, and mash it gently with the forceps on a clean piece of paper. *Safety Tip:* Be careful with the glass slide and coverslip. Place the lichen in the drop of water on the slide. Observe the lichen using the microscope under low and high power and describe and draw the structure of the lichen in your *Activity Log*. What organisms that you have observed does the lichen resemble? What organism other than fungi did you notice? What can you conclude about the relationship between these organisms? How would you define a lichen?

In the lichen you observed in the Try This Activity on the previous page, you saw that some fungi seem to exist in a relationship with other organisms. The fungus you observed lives and interacts with cyanobacteria or green algae, organisms capable of making their own food. The fungus and the cyanobacteria or green algae form a lichen. The fungus benefits from the association, because the cyanobacteria or green algae provide it with food. The cyanobacteria or green algae receive water, minerals, and solid support from the fungus.

Lichens vary from crusty or leaflike flakes less than a centimeter across to highly branched structures tens of centimeters across. They may be black, grey, bright green, orange, or yellowish. Lichens are often found covering rocks or on tree trunks, even on buildings, sidewalks, or tombstones. In some areas of the world, such as near the North Pole, they are the major form of vegetation. The fungus in lichens secretes chemicals that cause the surfaces of rocks to break down. The crumbled rock becomes part of the soil. Lichens begin the first steps in the formation of new soil from bare rock.

Lichens are actually two intertwined organisms, a fungus and cyanobacteria or green algae.

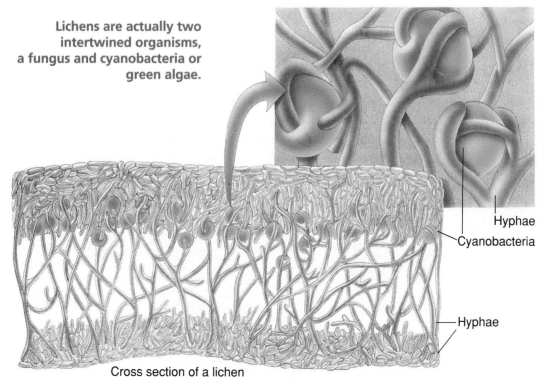

Hyphae
Cyanobacteria

Hyphae

Cross section of a lichen

Human Use of Fungi

Scientists have used substances produced by fungi to make medicines that save human lives. In 1928 the British scientist Alexander Fleming was growing bacteria on a medium, or substance full of nutrients, in petri dishes in his laboratory. In one dish, he observed that the medium had been contaminated by a fungus. Looking closer he noticed that the bacteria were not growing in the part of the dish surrounding this fungus.

During the next year, he investigated the cause of this phenomena. He found that the fungus was producing a substance that could stop bacteria from growing and could also kill bacteria. He tested samples of the nutrient medium that had contained the fungus on other bacteria and showed that many disease-causing bacteria could be killed by it. However, the medium, or what it contained, did not harm animals or people. Fleming had discovered an antibiotic. It was named penicillin after the fungus, *Penicillium,* which had produced it. *Penicillium* is a mold that commonly grows on oranges and other fruit.

Although scientists understood that penicillin might be used to cure bacterial infections in humans, only small, impure amounts of it could be obtained by growing the mold in culture dishes. In 1938 Howard Florey, another British scientist, purified penicillin from a culture mixture at Oxford University. Soon after, he and other scientists invented a way of manufacturing large amounts of penicillin economically. Penicillin could then be made available to doctors to treat bacterial infections.

Humans find many uses for fungi besides the antibacterial substances they produce. Do the Try This Activity on the next page to observe a property of some fungi that is very useful to humans.

The fungus at the top of the dish is producing a substance that prevents bacteria from growing around it.

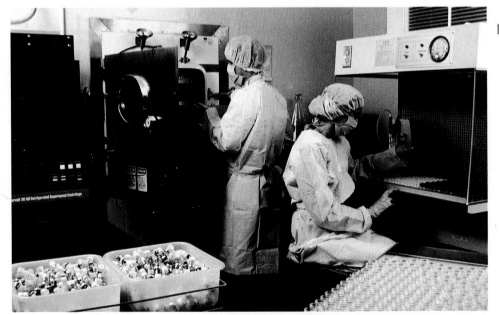

Penicillin to treat bacterial infections is produced in labs like these.

Activity!

Watching Yeast React

Yeast don't look alive, nor do they look like molds, mushrooms, or other fungi. Nevertheless, you will see that these fungi are very familiar and important to you.

What You Need

1/2 tsp. dry yeast, warm water, 2 test tubes, tall jar, 1/4 tsp. sugar, graduated cylinder, *Activity Log* page 26.

Observe the yeast and record its appearance in your *Activity Log*. Add 1/4 tsp. yeast and 10 mL water to each test tube. Place the test tubes in the jar. Add 1/4 tsp. of sugar to one tube and observe the tubes for 10 min. Record all observations and explanations in your *Activity Log*.

Yeast is a common, important fungus in your life because its ability to release carbon dioxide gas is used to make bread rise. This gas is responsible for the little holes you see in bread, which makes it light in texture. Without yeast, bread would be more like pita bread in texture.

When you did the Try This Activity above, how did you explain the action of yeast when sugar and water were added to it, compared to when only water was added? The result must have been due to the sugar added to the yeast. As in the activity described on pages 8 and 9 in the Introduction to this unit, the bubbles produced were carbon dioxide gas, released by the yeast in the process of respiration. When given a food source and water, yeast undergoes respiration without oxygen, and produces carbon dioxide. Sugar provided a food source for the yeast in the Try This Activity above.

The activity of fungi on foods is also responsible for making cheeses, soy sauce, and tofu. How many food products do you have at home that are made with fungi? Did you have anything to eat today that was produced by fungi? Mushrooms and truffles are fungi that are eaten as they are. If you enjoy mushrooms in salads, sauteed on steak or hamburgers, or in many other foods, read the career feature on the next page to find out whom you can thank.

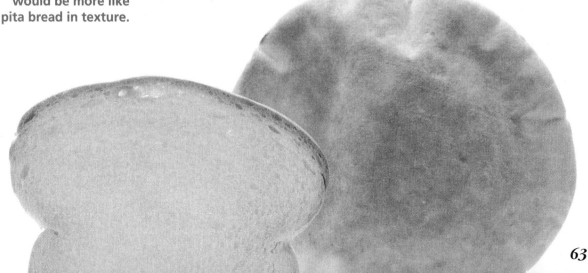

Mushroom Farmer

Mushroom farm

John Choi enjoys his work because he loves mushrooms!

Have you ever thought of how food is grown and gets to your table? You may have seen corn or vegetables growing on a farm. What about mushrooms? How are they farmed?

What is your vision of farming—long days under a bright sky, driving tractors or combines across acres of fields? How about hanging around in a dark cave or an abandoned coal mine over a bed of horse manure? Sound like fun? Sounds like a mushroom farmer.

John Choi spends a lot of time in a dark, damp basement as he runs his family mushroom farm. His unusual working conditions take into account the needs of fungi—darkness, moisture, warmth, and decaying organic matter as a source of food. Some mushroom farmers do actually grow their crops in caves and abandoned coal mines, where darkness, temperature, and moisture remain steady. However, they are also grown in mushroom houses and in cellars such as the Choi family's, where these conditions can be controlled. Mushroom spores may be planted in a bin of horse manure that is mixed with soil or hay.

A mushroom farmer must know not only how to create the proper growing conditions for mushrooms, but also how to identify different species of mushrooms. While many mushrooms are not only edible but are delicacies, others contain deadly toxins.

Mushroom farmers are also business people. Farms like John Choi's provide grocery stores, restaurants, and gourmet food stores with various species of delicious, and often expensive, mushrooms. John Choi needs to know how to market his product and run a business.

To prepare for his career as a mushroom farmer, John Choi took biology and business courses in high school, and studied botany and mushroom cultivation at a university. If you're interested in more information about a career growing or gathering mushrooms, you can get further information by writing to this address:

Mushroom Growers Cooperative Association
P.O. Box 375
Kennett Square, PA 19348

Sum It Up

• •

Simple organisms classified in the Kingdom Fungi are made of cells with cell walls and digest other organisms by releasing chemicals, then absorbing the nutrients for food. The four types of fungi are yeasts, mushrooms, molds, and water molds and mildews. Fungi reproduce asexually with spores as well as by producing sex cells.

Fungi interact with other organisms in a variety of important ways. They decompose dead organisms, releasing their nutrients to be used by other organisms. They feed on living organisms, causing disease in animals and plants. Some diseases have enormous consequences for humans, such as the Irish potato famine, ergot, or rusts and smuts on modern commercial crops. The fungus *Penicillium* produces the antibiotic penicillin, which has saved millions of human lives in this century because of its ability to kill bacteria. As with all simple organisms, the interactions between fungi and other organisms can be harmful or helpful in many environments.

Using Vocabulary

fungi
spores

Write a short paragraph describing fungi and their methods of reproduction, correctly using the words *fungi* and *spores* and their definitions. How are the four groups alike, and how are they different?

Critical Thinking

1. Explain how a spore may develop into a full-grown fungus hundreds of miles from its parent fungus.
2. What would happen in a forest ecosystem if all the fungi were killed suddenly by a disease? How could you counteract the effects?
3. What conditions would affect the growth or spread of fungal diseases in crops? What ways other than the ones mentioned in the text could be used to control such diseases?
4. Why would fungi produce antibiotics?
5. How can you cut down on fungus growth in your home or on your body?

Viruses-
Cell Invaders

This squash plant is interacting with its environment in many ways. It's using sunlight and water from the soil, and various animals may feed on it. Some interactions you can easily observe—and some you can't. The photographs on the next page show an interaction that happens inside the plant.

Can you imagine something that seems alive—but isn't? Viruses are so much simpler than the simple organisms you have observed so far that they must interact with living cells in order to reproduce. This interaction has important consequences for all organisms on Earth.

Minds On! What do the objects in the photograph on the bottom right remind you of—marbles? Alien spacecraft? In your *Activity Log* on page 27, list two or three things the photograph resembles. Make a guess about what they are made of.

Do those objects look like something that can grow? Marbles and spacecraft are nonliving, and can't grow anywhere. Of the two or three things these objects reminded you of, which are living things that can grow?●

The bottom right photograph shows what is inside the leaf causing the curved edges. An interaction between the particles shown in the photograph and the squash leaf is causing changes in the leaf. How do you think this is affecting the squash plant?

The bottom right photograph was taken with an electron microscope that magnifies things many more times than a light microscope does. It's not easy to see these structures! How can you explore them? Scientists often use models to explain something that's not easy to see or understand. A model can be a mental image of what something is like, or an object that has enough of the characteristics of what is being modeled that a scientist can learn from it.

Early astronomers made a mental model of the solar system that showed the sun, moon, and other planets moving around Earth in circles. Geographers can predict from using a globe, a physical model of Earth, that if anyone walks in one direction on Earth and keeps walking long enough, he or she will eventually return to the same spot. A model doesn't have all the properties of what it describes, but it helps us to understand it. Can you think of other examples of models that you use?

The first models of the solar system were not accurate. Today, astronomers know that the moon orbits Earth and all the planets orbit the sun. A model changes as more information about the object or process it represents is obtained. You have made some guesses about the structure of the particles shown on this page. You may have an idea about what they are doing in the squash. As you go through this lesson, you will gather more information that may change these ideas.

Does this leaf look healthy?

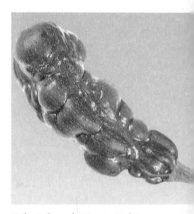

What has happened to this squash?

226,250X

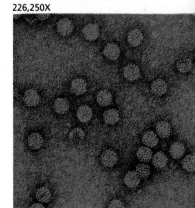

In this lesson you'll learn how these particles interact with the plant.

Activity!

Can You Model a Virus?

You can make a model of a virus based on photographs that have been taken by scientists. The model will help you understand the structure of a virus and speculate how it functions.

What You Need

small balloon
5-cm foam ball
1–2 sheets construction paper
5 pipe cleaners
straw
scissors
pencil
metric ruler
1 manila folder or cardboard
glue
transparent tape
Activity Log pages 28–29

What To Do

1 Look carefully at the photo and illustration at the top of the next page. This object has been observed by scientists through an electron microscope. In order to learn more about this strange object, you need to make a three-dimensional model of it. First, make a list of the parts you can see. Measure each part.

2 Using the materials provided, or any others that you think would work better, design a model of this structure. Before you start to work, list the materials you plan to use to construct it. Make sure the proportions of the model are accurate. Then build your model. You can change your plans as you go along. *Safety Tip:* Use care with scissors.

Safety!

See the *Safety Tip* in step 2.

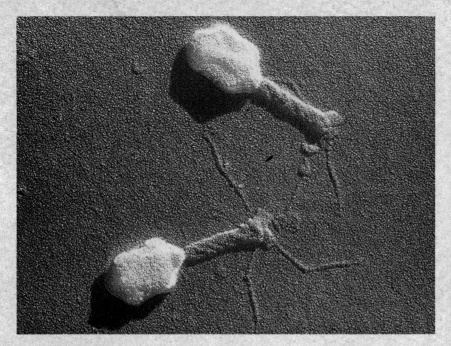

Scientists have taken this photograph of a virus using an electron microscope.

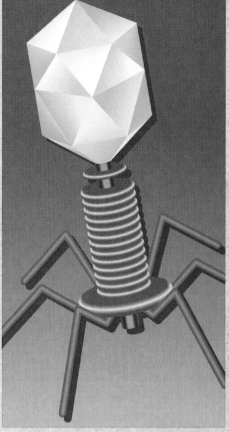

Use this computer-generated illustration of the same virus as a guide to build a model of it.

What Happened?

1. Compare your finished model with the photo and drawing. Describe how your model is different from them, and how it is the same.
2. Compare your model with your classmates' models. Is there one that is closer to the photo and drawing than yours? How is yours better? Describe in your *Activity Log* any way you could improve your model.
3. In your *Activity Log,* list ways your model is not like a real virus.

What Now?

1. Compare your model of a virus to a typical animal cell. In your *Activity Log,* list the differences between them.
2. Are there any structures on your virus model that remind you of cells? Speculate what you think the different parts of the virus do.
3. Do you think a virus could reproduce, digest or produce food, or move? Use what you know about viruses at this point, and develop a hypothesis about what a virus is. Don't worry about being wrong—scientists make predictions based on the information they have at the moment, and then change their ideas as new information is gathered.
4. Write two or three problem statements or questions about viruses you would like to be able to answer.

Modeling a Virus

Was your model a good representation of a virus? You can tell if it looks like a virus, but you can't tell if it works like a virus, or what substances make up a virus. When you made the model, you based it on the information you had at the time about a particular virus—a photograph and drawing. You didn't have information about its functioning or composition. All models are limited by the evidence available to construct the model. As you go through this lesson, you can compare your model and hypotheses to new information you obtain about viruses. Your ideas about viruses will probably change!

After your model was finished, you compared it to the information you had and decided how you could make it more accurate. You shared your ideas with the other students in your class, and changed your model as you got new ideas. Scientists discovered the structure of viruses and how they interact with living things by experimenting according to scientific methods similar to the one you read about in the Introduction to this unit. They built models of what they thought viruses were like based on the information they gained, and changed their ideas as they gathered more information.

Scientists use filters in their research.

By the end of the 19th century, scientists were beginning to understand how microorganisms caused diseases. The microorganisms that caused many contagious diseases could be seen with a light microscope. However, although some diseases such as smallpox or rabies were contagious, no microorganisms could be identified through a light microscope that caused them.

In 1892 a Russian biologist, Dimitri Iwanowski (di mē′trē ē′vän ôf′skē), was studying a disease that affected plants, the tobacco mosaic disease. The leaves of tobacco plants that had this disease would get spots, shrivel up, and die. Iwanowski rubbed the juice of an affected plant onto the leaf of a healthy plant, and the healthy leaves soon showed signs of the disease. When he looked at the leaf juice under the microscope, he couldn't find any microorganism that could be responsible for this.

Iwanowski passed some of the leaf juice through a filter that had very small holes. Liquids could pass through the holes in the filter but microorganisms could not, because the holes were too small. The liquid that passed through this filter should have been free of the microorganisms that caused disease. However, the plant juice that passed through the filter was still able to cause the tobacco mosaic disease. What do you think Iwanowski concluded about the structure of the agent that caused tobacco mosaic disease from this result?

In 1935 an American scientist, Wendell Stanley, demonstrated that the things that caused this disease, which had been named viruses, could be made to form crystals if many were lumped together. Scientists knew that simple chemicals could form crystals, but there was no evidence that living things made of cells could crystallize. Therefore, scientists concluded that viruses couldn't be made of cells.

Based on the information gathered by scientists at this point, a virus seemed to be like a nonliving chemical in structure. However, it appeared to be able to reproduce, which is a characteristic of living things. In this half-century, with the development of the electron microscope, biologists have been able to see viruses. Even more recently, viruses have been analyzed chemically, taken apart, and put back together. Because of this research, scientists know more about their structure and the ways they cause disease.

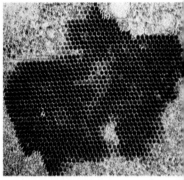

54,600X

Crystals of viruses, similar to those Wendell Stanley produced

These photographs of viruses have been taken through an electron microscope.

175,000X

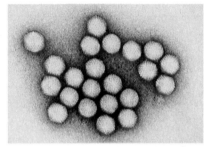

200,000X

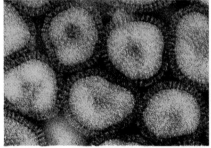

736,000X

62,000X

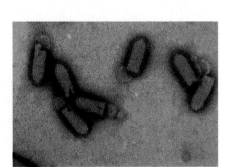

334,000X

What Is a Virus?

When you looked at the photographs of particles in the squash leaf on page 67, did you think the particles were alive? When you built your model of a virus, did you compare it to a cell and speculate whether it could reproduce or not? A **virus** is a particle made up of hereditary material and protein that reproduces only within a living cell. Viruses aren't made of cells, are much smaller than any cell, and are difficult to classify because they have characteristics of both living and nonliving things. The chart on this page compares the characteristics of cells and viruses. Notice that viruses have different characteristics when they are inside cells. A virus has hereditary material and contains proteins, as all living things do. But all living things can reproduce on their own, and a virus can't. For this reason viruses aren't classified in any kingdom, but in a group by themselves.

The illustration at the bottom of the page compares a virus to a cell. A virus has two parts. The inside of a virus is made up of hereditary material, and the outside is a protein coat. In a virus, the proteins are arranged into a solid shell. The protein coat protects the hereditary material and gives the virus its characteristic shape. The photographs on the previous page show some of the shapes viruses can take. What you modeled in the Explore Activity on pages 68 and 69 was the protein coat of one virus. Its hereditary material was inside the coat.

Charateristics of Living Things

Living Things	Cells	Viruses Outside Cells	Viruses Inside Cells
Take energy from the environment	YES	NO	NO
Excrete wastes	YES	NO	NO
Respond to environment	YES	NO	NO
Reproduce	YES	NO	YES
Grow and develop	YES	NO	NO
Made of cells	YES	NO	NO

This chart lists the characteristics all living things share. How do viruses compare to cells? Can you speculate why viruses have different characteristics when they are within cells? You will read more about this later. Are viruses alive or not?

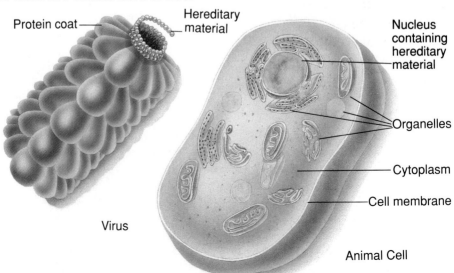

Although this drawing doesn't depict the actual size difference between a virus and a cell, you can compare the features of a cell and a virus. What does the cell have that the virus doesn't?

Protein coat — Hereditary material

Virus

Nucleus containing hereditary material

Organelles

Cytoplasm

Cell membrane

Animal Cell

How Do Viruses Reproduce?

In order to reproduce, a part of a virus must get inside a cell. When a virus comes in contact with a cell, the virus's protein coat attaches to the cell's surface. When you made your model, what did you guess the structures on the virus that stuck out on one end like legs were used for? This particular virus uses these structures to attach to a cell. Once it has attached, the hereditary material of the virus enters the cell. The protein coat usually stays outside.

Inside the cell, the hereditary material of the virus takes over the cell. You can visualize how this happens if you imagine the virus as a robot that breaks into an automobile factory and takes over the management of the factory. The robot does nothing except give orders that the workers in the factory carry out. The robot gives the workers a set of instructions to construct robots, using the tools and materials in the factory. The factory no longer produces automobiles—only robots, just like the robot that took over the factory. When they are assembled, the new robots leave the factory to take over more factories and order more robots to be produced.

The hereditary material of the virus uses a cell to produce more viruses, as the robot in the analogy used the factory to produce more robots. Hereditary material is like a set of instructions for making something. The hereditary material of the virus provides instructions for the cell to make more viruses, like the robot provided a set of instructions for making robots. The virus's protein coat and its hereditary material are made separately in the cell, and the proteins form a coat around each set of hereditary material. The result is a batch of new viruses.

The reproductive cycle of some viruses can take place within 25 minutes.

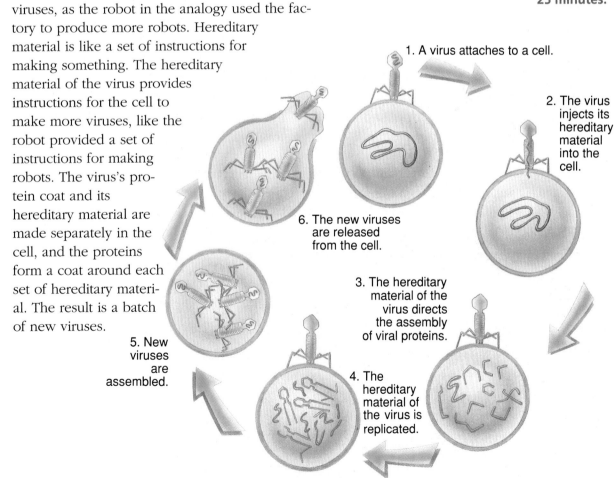

1. A virus attaches to a cell.

2. The virus injects its hereditary material into the cell.

3. The hereditary material of the virus directs the assembly of viral proteins.

4. The hereditary material of the virus is replicated.

5. New viruses are assembled.

6. The new viruses are released from the cell.

What Effect Does a Virus Have on Cells?

Human

Colds, flu
Measles
Mumps
Chicken pox
Hepatitis
Cold sores
AIDS
Warts
Rabies

Other Animals

Distemper
Foot & mouth
  disease
Feline leukemia
Rabies

Plants

Turnip yellow
  mosaic
Tobacco mosaic
Cucumber mosaic
Apple mosaic
Chrysanthemum
  mottle disease

How many of these diseases caused by viruses are you familiar with?

What happens to a cell that is infected with a virus? The virus may be destroyed by a cell before it can reproduce. If the virus starts to reproduce, the normal functioning of the cell may be disrupted. The cell may break open, releasing new viruses, which can then infect other cells. Sometimes, new viruses are released from the infected cell over time, without destroying the cell. If these processes happened in the cells of a plant or animal, how would they affect it?

The hereditary material of some viruses becomes part of the hereditary material of the cell it infects. Some of these viruses cause cells to begin to reproduce rapidly, resulting in a mass of tissue, for example a wart or a tumor. Other viruses may not reproduce for a long time. One type of herpes virus, which causes the common cold sore, may be present in nerve cells of the lips for a long time before reproducing. Stress triggers the formation of a cold sore. Many people carry this virus and never develop a cold sore at all. How serious could these types of infections be for an organism?

These interactions between viruses and cells affect all cellular organisms on Earth, from bacteria to humans. When a virus infects an organism, disease usually results. The seriousness of the disease depends on the type of virus. Some viruses infect only one kind of organism. The model you made was of a virus that infects only bacteria. Look at the chart of viral diseases on this page. Which diseases do you think are specific to one organism? Some viruses can attach to many kinds of cells. Which diseases listed in the chart could infect your cells or your dog's cells? Some viruses will only enter one type of cell within an organism, for example the HIV virus only lives in a specific type of blood cell in a human.

Many plants, for example cucumbers and apple trees, are affected by viral diseases. Plant viruses may be spread by wind or insects such as aphids or beetles that chew on or suck juice out of the plant. The break in the plant cell wall allows a virus to enter, and the insect may take a virus into its body with the plant material it is eating. Usually it's not possible to treat a viral plant disease. The best that farmers can do when they have an infected plant is to destroy it so the disease won't spread further.

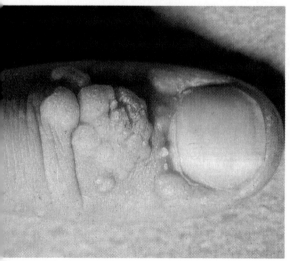

Some viruses cause minor problems, such as the warts depicted on the left, and others, like feline leukemia, are fatal.

Could humans make use of these interactions between viruses and cells? Read the Focus on Technology feature below to discover how the ability of a virus to infect a bacterium has been used by some scientists.

Focus on Technology

Genetic Engineering— a Microscopic Insulin Factory

Have you heard the term *genetic engineering?* About 15 years ago, scientists developed a technique to remove some genetic or hereditary material from one organism and insert it into another. Hereditary material is like a blueprint, or set of instructions for producing a protein. Scientists carefully choose hereditary material that will produce the protein they want, and insert it into a bacterium. The bacterium then produces the protein.

Does that sound like the way a virus works? One way scientists insert hereditary material into a bacterium is to attach hereditary material to a virus that will infect a bacterium, like the one you modeled in the Explore Activity on pages 68 and 69. The virus carries the hereditary material into the bacterium. Scientists can choose a virus that won't destroy the bacterium. The bacterium reproduces the hereditary material and produces proteins from it.

Today, bacteria are used as factories to produce many kinds of proteins. One wonderful way that genetic engineering has helped us is in the production of insulin. Millions of people have the disease diabetes. A person with this disease isn't able to make a protein called insulin (in′sə lin), which is needed by the body to use sugar in the production of energy. Diabetes can be life-threatening if not treated. Injections of insulin, however, will treat the disease.

For a long time, insulin to treat diabetes was taken from pigs. Unfortunately, some people are allergic to pig insulin. Scientists took the human hereditary material that is a blueprint for insulin and inserted it into a bacterium. The result was a microscopic insulin factory. The bacterium produced human insulin that was gathered and injected into diabetics. Since human insulin was being produced, there was no allergic reaction.

Why not make the insulin by a chemical process? It is very difficult to make proteins from scratch. Insulin made this way would be much more expensive than that made by bacteria.

The Immune System—
Your Body Fights Back

Virus

Interferon

Infected cell

The last time you had a cold, did you get medicine from a doctor? Unless you had a bacterial infection also, the doctor probably gave you medicines to treat the symptoms, like cough medicine or a decongestant, and instructed you to rest and drink lots of liquids. Antibiotics can kill bacteria, but there are few medications that will kill viruses. If you are infected with a virus, you have to rely on your body to fight the infection.

Your body has defenses against viruses. As with microorganisms, your skin acts as a barrier to keep most viruses away from your body cells. Even when a virus attacks a living cell within your body, that cell tries to defend itself. The system your body uses to defend itself against viruses and simple organisms is the **immune** (i mūn′) **system.** The immune system consists of a substance called interferon, white blood cells, and substances called antibodies and complement, which circulate in your blood or other body fluids.

Many of your body cells produce a protein called interferon (in′tər fîr′ on), which prevents viruses from spreading or tumors from growing. Interferon is a first line of defense against viral infections. The protein is named interferon because it interferes with viruses. Within a few hours of the time a virus enters a cell, the cell begins to make interferon. The interferon is released from the infected cell and causes nearby cells to produce proteins that prevent the viruses from reproducing. This process prevents the virus from spreading.

When new viruses are released from an infected cell, interferon is also released. Interferon helps other cells fight off the invading viruses.

A **white blood cell** is a cell found in the bloodstream that destroys microorganisms or substances that are not part of the body. When a cell in your body is infected with a virus, certain white blood cells can detect that it is infected and will destroy it.

Antibodies (an′ti bod′ēz) are proteins made by certain white blood cells. One way antibodies protect the body is to stick to viruses and prevent them from attaching to cells. If the viruses can't attach, they can't enter the cells and cause disease. Do the Try This Activity on the next page to observe this principle.

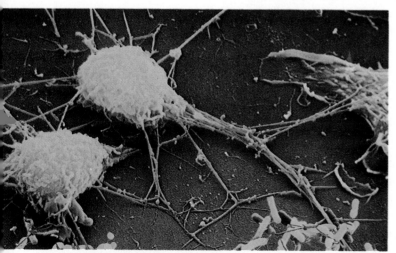

White blood cells engulf bacteria using pseudopods, the same cellular extensions amoebas use to move and eat.

Activity!

How To Stop a Virus...

You can make a model that will demonstrate the way antibodies prevent viruses from infecting cells.

What You Need

masking tape
1-in. diameter foam ball
2-in. diameter foam ball
3-in. diameter foam ball
2 ½-in. self-gripping adhesive-backed fasteners
Activity Log **page 30**

Using the masking tape, label the largest ball "cell," the medium one "virus," and the smallest one "antibody." Attach one of the soft, fabric-loop sides of one fastener to the "cell" by its adhesive backing. Attach a rough side of one fastener, (the side with hooks) to the "virus" by its adhesive backing. Stick the virus onto the cell using the fasteners. What do the fasteners represent? Attach the soft side of the second fastener to an "antibody." When would a virus not be able to bind to a cell? Pull the "virus" off, and attach an "antibody" to the virus. Can the virus bind to the cell now? Where else can the antibody bind? Under what conditions would an antibody bind there?

Antibodies also act in another way to defend the body against viruses. If an antibody attaches to a cell that has been infected by a virus, the antibody acts like a flag that marks the cell for destruction. The cell can be destroyed in several ways. White blood cells can recognize the antibodies and destroy the cell. A protein substance called complement that circulates in the blood also recognizes antibodies. Complement can destroy the cell to which the antibodies are attached. Since it takes days, or even months, after a viral infection for antibodies to form, this part of the immune system is a slow response to an infection by viruses.

Once your immune system has reacted to a virus, it will react to that same virus every time it enters your body, and it will react more rapidly each time, preventing the virus from causing the disease. If your immune system has reacted to a particular virus in this way, you are said to be immune to the disease caused by that virus, because it can't infect you again. For example, if you have already had the measles, your body has produced antibodies to the virus that causes measles. If the measles virus enters your body again, the antibodies should recognize it, bind to it, and prevent it from giving you the disease again.

Scientists have developed ways to use your immune system to protect you before you come in contact with dangerous viruses or bacteria. A **vaccine** (vak sēn′) is a substance that sets up your immune system to produce antibodies to the invading substance. Vaccines are made from viruses or bacterial toxins. Dead or weakened viruses or neutralized toxins are used because they either don't cause a person to have the disease, or they cause only a mild case of the disease. For example, when you've been given the measles vaccine, you've been immunized, or made immune to, measles. You've produced antibodies to the measles virus, just as you would have if you had contracted the disease naturally. Therefore, you should not develop the disease measles. A tetanus vaccine causes your body to produce antibodies to the toxin produced by the bacteria that cause the disease tetanus. If the toxin enters your body later, the antibody will neutralize the toxin.

Minds On! What immunizations have you had? In your *Activity Log* on page 31, list as many as you can remember. Then, check with your parent or guardian to complete the list.●

Vaccines have not been developed for all viruses. Scientists haven't been able to weaken some viruses enough to make a vaccine from them that would not cause a disease. It would be wonderful if there were a vaccine for the common cold, but there are so many kinds of viruses that cause colds, it would be impossible to immunize against them all.

Scientists who study the immune system develop vaccines. Read the career feature below for more information on the subjects such scientists research. Then read the feature on the next page to find out about a disease caused by a virus infecting part of the immune system.

CAREERS Immunologist _____

Much of our knowledge about the way the body fights viruses comes from work done by immunologists (im′yə nol′ə jests), scientists who study the immune system. To be an immunologist like Martha Thompson, you must go to college and take science courses, especially those in biology and chemistry. After graduation you must go to graduate school to earn a Ph.D. degree in immunology.

Dr. Thompson researches how interferon acts in fighting viruses. She develops mental and physical models of the action of interferon, based on the results of her experiments. She shares ideas with researchers from as far away as Hong Kong, Sweden, and Nigeria.

All over the world, immunologists are studying diseases like hepatitis, which are caused by viruses, and diseases like some cancers and arthritis, which are not known to be caused by viruses, but involve the immune system. These scientists are asking questions like "Can the immune system be made to fight cancer or viruses more effectively?"

A Virus That Infects the Immune System

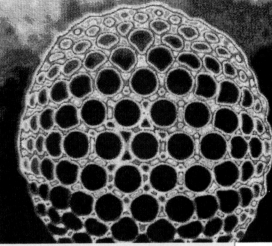

121,000X

Have you heard of the disease AIDS? AIDS stands for acquired immune deficiency syndrome. The immune system of a person with AIDS is not working as well as it should.

The virus that causes AIDS is called HIV, or Human Immunodeficiency Virus. It causes the disease by entering and killing white blood cells. Since these are the cells that fight infections, a person with AIDS has no defense against disease. Without a well-functioning immune system, the infected person eventually dies from diseases such as pneumonia or certain kinds of cancer.

Scientists worldwide are involved in AIDS research. At this time there is no cure for AIDS. Flossie Wong-Staal of the University of California at San Diego is one scientist who's working on developing a vaccine against HIV. The drug AZT is somewhat effective against AIDS. It slows down the rate at which HIV reproduces inside white blood cells. Therefore, the cells are not destroyed as quickly, and the virus doesn't spread as fast through the body. If AZT is given to an AIDS patient, the person's symptoms usually improve. He or she can hope to survive for a longer time. If a person is infected with the virus but not showing symptoms, AZT usually delays the onset of AIDS.

A computer-generated image of Human Immunodeficiency Virus, or HIV, the virus that causes the disease AIDS. Flossie Wong-Staal's research helped determine the structure of the virus, making this image possible.

All evidence indicates that AIDS can only be caught by coming into contact with the blood or body fluids of an infected person. This may occur during unsafe sexual contact, when a contaminated needle is used for an injection, or from a blood transfusion in which the blood is contaminated. A pregnant woman who has the HIV virus can pass it on to her fetus.

Many people who are infected with HIV don't show any symptoms of AIDS for many years. They can be healthy for up to ten years after being infected. A simple blood test can detect antibodies to the virus. Unfortunately, antibodies may not develop until several months after the virus has entered the body, and the virus can be transmitted to another person even if the disease hasn't developed.

5,250X

A white blood cell (massive body) being attacked by HIV (small green bodies)

Public Health Laws

In the past there were policies that required doctors to report cases of certain diseases to government health agencies. In some cases, people who had contagious diseases like tuberculosis, a disease affecting the lungs, were placed in quarantine, or isolation, from people who weren't infected. There were no medicines that could cure tuberculosis at the time, and doctors felt it was important to prevent it from spreading.

Some people believe it would be a good idea to have a policy in the United States about testing for HIV, or even to quarantine people who are infected. Other people believe this is unrealistic, violates the rights of those who are infected, and may do more harm than good.

Form groups of four with your classmates. As citizens, you are concerned about preventing the spread of HIV. You know some information about viruses and AIDS. Discuss the possibility of a public health policy that would help control the spread of HIV. Together, write a public health policy that will apply for the entire United States. Does your policy include AIDS/HIV education as well as community and medical interventions? Is your policy sensitive to individual needs? Is it realistic?

The disease AIDS has quickly spread around the world through international travel, business, and immigration. Today, the world is a small place. All humans benefit from the ideas, goods, and services we import from other societies around the globe. Unfortunately, we take our contagious diseases with us when we go. Would your public health policy about AIDS affect international travel? Do you think it should?

In the past there were no effective treatments or a vaccine for the disease polio, and people who had the virus that caused it were often isolated.

The Importance of Immunity

You've probably never seen a person infected with smallpox, and it's not likely you ever will. Smallpox no longer exists. At one time this serious viral disease was common in Europe. The smallpox virus produced pus-filled sores and a dangerously high fever. Many people died from this disease, and those who survived had deep, pit-like scars where the sores had been. Smallpox was also very contagious.

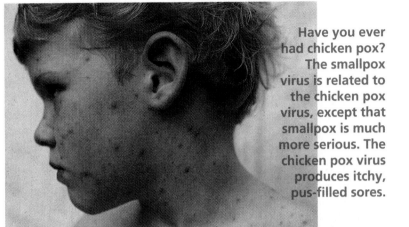

What happens when a virus is present in your body for the first time? Or when you are vaccinated against a virus? What would happen if you were not vaccinated against a virus and it entered your body? As Europeans explored and colonized the world, they brought smallpox, among other diseases, with them. Some of them were immune to smallpox because they had already had the disease. They could carry the virus and not get sick from it. But they could pass it on to other people who did not have immunity to it.

Smallpox developed in Europe and had never existed in America until it was brought by European colonists. None of the Native Americans had any antibodies to this virus. When a Native American was infected with the virus, it was deadly. If one member of a tribe became infected, smallpox would often sweep through an entire village or tribe. Sometimes whole tribes were wiped out by smallpox. Read the Literature Link on the next page to get a better idea of the effects smallpox, or any disease like smallpox, could have on a society.

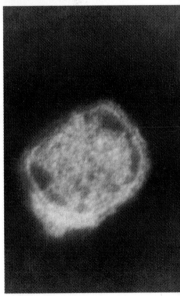

44,200X **Virus that causes smallpox**

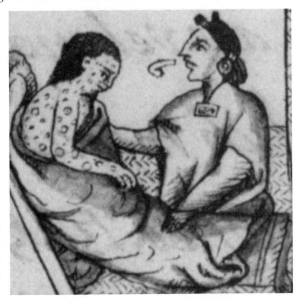

Lack of immunity to the smallpox virus resulted in entire Native American villages being wiped out.

Can a fifteen-year-old girl save her people?

SWEETGRASS

Jan Hudson

SCHOLASTIC

Literature Link

Sweetgrass

Sweetgrass by Jan Hudson tells of a 19th century Blackfoot Indian teenager, her family, and the ravages of smallpox upon their tribe after the warriors traded at an outpost fort. Read the story to help you understand the disease and its effect on a society. As you read, pay attention to the Blackfoot beliefs about how smallpox was spread, and how it could be treated. Using what you know about viruses, how accurate were their ideas?

Imagine you are a Blackfoot and have heard stories told by the elders of the tribe of a previous smallpox epidemic. Retell the story of how the disease was brought into your village, who was the first to be infected, how you coped with the disease, and what happened after the epidemic passed. How had your village changed? Use correct grammar, punctuation, and spelling—and your imagination!

Edward Jenner developed the first vaccine.

For many years smallpox remained a devastating problem with no good solution. In the late 18th century in England, a family doctor named Edward Jenner noticed that people who came down with a mild disease, cowpox, never developed smallpox. Cowpox produced mild symptoms, more like chicken pox than smallpox. Jenner hypothesized from this observation that if a person were deliberately infected with a cowpox virus, he or she could not catch smallpox.

Jenner took some pus from a sore on a woman infected with cowpox and put it into a cut on the hand of a boy. The boy developed cowpox. What did the pus contain to transmit the disease? Later Jenner did an experiment that doctors today would not do because it is so dangerous—he infected the boy with pus from a smallpox sore. Fortunately, the boy did not develop smallpox!

When the boy was infected with the cowpox virus, he developed antibodies to it. The smallpox virus is very similar to cowpox, and the antibodies attacked smallpox viruses when they were present in his body. He had become immune to smallpox by being exposed to a similar virus.

After this, the smallpox vaccine was used widely all over the world. As people were immunized against smallpox, the disease became rare. Antibodies didn't allow the virus to reproduce in anyone who had been vaccinated. If the virus couldn't reproduce, it couldn't spread. Today, the World Health Organization has declared that this disease can't be found anywhere in the world. Smallpox no longer exists!

Sum It Up

Scientists often use models to describe objects or phenomena that are not easily observed in a laboratory, or to test their hypotheses. A model is based on the most accurate information available about what it represents, and it changes as more information becomes available. A model that shows that a virus is composed of a core of hereditary material and a protein coat can be used to demonstrate that viruses are nonliving particles.

Because they consist of only hereditary material and protein, it's impossible for viruses to reproduce unless they are within a living cell. Viruses reproduce by taking over living cells. Animals react to infection by viruses with their immune system. Since the cell is often disrupted or killed by the interaction with a virus, an infected organism often develops a disease. This disease-causing interaction makes viruses extremely important to all organisms.

Using Vocabulary

antibodies
immune system
vaccine
virus
white blood cell

Develop a crossword puzzle using the vocabulary words from this section, and as many other important words from the lesson as you can. When you are finished, exchange your crossword puzzle with a friend and complete them.

Critical Thinking

1. How could your model of a virus be changed so it would model the way viruses reproduce?
2. If your body could not make interferon, how would your immune response to a viral infection be different?
3. Why don't scientists develop vaccines for most bacterial diseases?
4. How would Native Americans have been affected by smallpox if they had been exposed to cows infected with cowpox?
5. Why can't scientists develop a drug that kills viruses after they have infected a cell?

A Crucial Part of Life on Earth

Now you are aware of a world of simple organisms covering three distinct kingdoms of life, and of some strange particles that exist on the border between the living and nonliving worlds. Although most of these can't be seen by the unaided eye, they are in food we eat, on the clothes we wear, in air we breathe, even in and on our bodies.

Minds On! On page 7 in the Introduction to this unit, you thought about what the world might be like without simple organisms and viruses. In groups of four to six, using the information covered in this unit, discuss again how you think the world would be different without simple organisms and viruses. Have your ideas changed?●

Simple organisms are like you in some ways. All simple organisms carry on the same life activities as larger organisms, including humans. These activities include respiration, growth, reproduction, the ability to respond to their surroundings, and the ability to cause changes in their surroundings. Viruses can't carry on these activities independently, however. Viruses affect all organisms because they need living cells to reproduce. This interaction sometimes causes disease in plants and animals, and affects simple organisms, too.

It's impossible to find simple organisms that don't affect other organisms through their interactions. Do the Try This Activity below to put together all the interactions you have read about in this unit.

In this unit you have studied the simple organisms monerans, protists, fungi, and the particles called viruses that have some characteristics of life under some conditions.

TRY THIS

Activity!

Picture This Interaction

Simple organisms and viruses have a variety of roles on Earth. They affect each other as well as plants and animals. See how many of these relationships you can depict in a collage or drawing.

What You Need

old magazines, crayons, markers, or colored pencils
18 in. × 24 in. newsprint paper
scissors, if needed
glue, if needed

Create a collage or a drawing showing the relationships between monerans, protists, fungi, viruses, plants, and animals. The relationships overlap and impact each other—think about this also when you plan your collage or drawing.

How have you interacted with simple organisms today? Have you taken penicillin, produced by a fungus? Have you eaten yogurt, produced with the help of bacteria? Did you wash the dishes to control the growth of microorganisms?

Although some simple organisms cause diseases and destroy human food or belongings, our very lives depend on others. Plants and other animals depend on them also, to provide nutrients in the soil, oxygen in the air, and a valuable food source. Besides their important roles in environments on Earth, simple organisms have been used by scientists to make foods and medicines. Do the Try This Activity below to invent new ways to use simple organisms or viruses.

TRY THIS Activity!

Putting Simple Organisms to Work

Imagine it's 2002, and you are a microbiologist who has just been hired by a major corporation to invent new applications for simple organisms and viruses. Now is a good time to develop new products. We are dealing with pollution, fierce global competition, a large human population, and shortages in many natural resources. New ideas are needed! Additionally, a group of nations has begun a space colony on the moon. This colony will conduct research and will be a prototype for further colonization in space. A potentially vast marketplace has opened up.

What You Need
Activity Log page 32

Your job is to invent as many new applications for simple organisms and viruses as you can, both on Earth and in enclosed environments being created in space. You can create new products, or find a new way to use simple organisms or viruses to meet an environmental need. What is needed on Earth and in space colonies? What characteristics of simple organisms and viruses can meet those needs? Could you use the organisms together in some way? Which would be the best organism for a particular job?

In your *Activity Log,* list as many uses as you can, and describe how you will go about creating the product or meeting the environmental need. As part of the process, describe what you will need to provide for the organisms or viruses to keep them alive or allow them to reproduce.

Finally, describe in your *Activity Log* how you will deal with any harmful effects the simple organisms or viruses might have on the environment.

You may want to use reference materials or your text to help you develop ideas. Share your ideas with the class when you are finished.

GLOSSARY

Use the pronunciation key below to help you decode, or read, the pronunciations.

Pronunciation Key

a	at, bad	d	dear, soda, bad
ā	ape, pain, day, break	f	five, defend, leaf, off, cough, elephant
ä	father, car, heart	g	game, ago, fog, egg
âr	care, pair, bear, their, where	h	hat, ahead
e	end, pet, said, heaven, friend	hw	white, whether, which
ē	equal, me, feet, team, piece, key	j	joke, enjoy, gem, page, edge
i	it, big, English, hymn	k	kite, bakery, seek, tack, cat
ī	ice, fine, lie, my	l	lid, sailor, feel, ball, allow
îr	ear, deer, here, pierce	m	man, family, dream
o	odd, hot, watch	n	not, final, pan, knife
ō	old, oat, toe, low	ng	long, singer, pink
ô	coffee, all, taught, law, fought	p	pail, repair, soap, happy
ôr	order, fork, horse, story, pour	r	ride, parent, wear, more, marry
oi	oil, toy	s	sit, aside, pets, cent, pass
ou	out, now	sh	shoe, washer, fish mission, nation
u	up, mud, love, double	t	tag, pretend, fat, button, dressed
ū	use, mule, cue, feud, few	th	thin, panther, both
ü	rule, true, food	th	this, mother, smooth
ù	put, wood, should	v	very, favor, wave
ûr	burn, hurry, term, bird, word,courage	w	wet, weather, reward
ə	about, taken, pencil, lemon, circus	y	yes, onion
b	bat, above, job	z	zoo, lazy, jazz, rose, dogs, houses
ch	chin, such, match	zh	vision, treasure, seizure

aerobic respiration (â rō′ bik res′ pə ra′ shən) a process in some living cells where oxygen is used to break food down into carbon dioxide and water, and release energy for life activities

AIDS (ādz) acquired immune deficiency syndrome, a human disease where the immune system becomes deficient after being infected with a virus

amoebas (ə mē′ bəs) A group of protozoans that move by forming pseudopods

anaerobic respiration (an′ â rō′ bik res′ pə rā′ shən) a process in some living cells where food is broken down to release energy for life activities without using oxygen

antibiotics (an′ tē bī ot′ iks) substances that kill or inhibit the growth of bacteria

antibodies (an′ ti bod′ ēz) proteins made by certain white blood cells that fight infections by microorganisms or viruses by preventing them from infecting cells, or by binding to infected cells to mark them for destruction

antiseptic (an′ ti sep′ tik) a substance that kills or prevents the growth of microorganisms on living tissue

bacilli (bə sil′ ī) rod-shaped bacteria

bacteria (bak tûr′ ē ə) organisms that are classified in the Kingdom Monera; may be either producers or consumers

biodegradable (bī′ ō di grā′ də bəl) can be decomposed by bacteria and other simple organisms

bioluminescence (bī ō lü mən nes sənts) the release of light from living organisms when certain energy containing substances are broken down in their cells.

capsule (kap′ səl) a sticky outer layer found on some bacteria that keeps the cell from drying out and helps it stick to its food source, or other cells

cell (sel) the basic unit of structure and function in an organism

cell membrane (sel mem′ brān) a thin layer that surrounds a cell

cell wall (sel wôl) a rigid layer that surrounds the cell membrane of monerans, plants, fungi, and some protists

chloroplast (klôr′ə plast′) the organelle of a plant cell where the process of photosynthesis takes place

cilia (sil′ ē ə) hair-like extensions of a cell that can move

cocci (kok′ sī) round bacteria

complement (kom′ plə mənt) a substance that circulates in the blood that destroys cells that have been infected with viruses by recognizing antibodies attached to the cells

consumers (kən sü′ mərz) organisms that acquire energy for survival and reproduction by eating other organisms

contagious (kən tā′ jəs) can be transmitted from one organism to another, as a disease

control (kən trōl′) a standard against which to compare the results obtained when testing the variable in an experiment

cyanobacteria (sī an′ō bak tîr′ ē ə) organisms classified in the Kingdom Monera that contain the pigment chlorophyll, make their own food through the process of photosynthesis or chemosynthesis

cytoplasm (sī tə plaz′ əm) the jelly-like substance within a cell membrane that may contain organelles and various substances

decomposers (dē′ kəm pō zərz) organisms that acquire energy by breaking down, or decomposing, dead organisms

diatomaceous (dī ət ə mā′ shəs) **earth** a substance made from the shells of diatoms that has industrial uses, also called diatomite

diatoms (dī′ ə tomz) a group of protists that form hard shells, undergo photosynthesis, are a major food source and an important source of oxygen

dinoflagellates (din′ ə flaj′ ə lāts′) a group of protists that form hard plates inside their cells, undergo photosynthesis, have two flagella at a right angle to each other, and are a food and oxygen source for other organisms

disinfectant (dis′ in fek′tənt) a substance that kills microorganisms on nonliving objects

endospores (en′dō spôrz) thick-walled structures that form in some bacteria around the hereditary material and a small amount of cytoplasm, and can survive harsh conditions for years before becoming active cells again

euglenoids (ū glē′ nöidz) a group of photosynthetic protists that have one or two flagella and a red stigma

fission (fish′ ən) the reproductive process of bacteria where hereditary material is copied and the cell divides into two identical cells

flagellates (flaj′ ə lāts) a group of protozoans that can move by whipping their one or more flagella back and forth

flagellum (flə jel′ əm) a long whip-like structure that extends from a cell and is used for movement

foraminiferans (fə ram′ ə nif′ ə rənz) amoebas that formed the shells that are found in the White Cliffs of Dover

fungi (fun′ jī) a kingdom of organisms that have cells with cell walls and digest materials by secreting enzymes, then absorbing the nutrients

genetic engineering (jə net′ ik en′ jə nîr′ ing) a process where hereditary material is inserted into a bacterium in order to produce proteins

gills (gilz) the part of a mushroom that contains the spore-producing structures

hereditary material (hə red′ i ter′ ē mə tîr′ ē əl) the material that provides instructions for making proteins and controls the activities of the cell

hyphae (hī′ fē) thin, winding, branching filaments made of cells in a fungus

hypothesis (hī poth′ə sis) a predicted answer to the problem statement of an experiment

immune system (i mūn′ sis′ təm) the system your body uses to defend itself against viruses and simple organisms, including a substance called interferon, white blood cells, and substances called antibodies and complement that circulate in your blood or other body fluids

immunologist (im′ yə nol′ ə jest) a scientist who studies the immune system

interferon (in′ tər fir′ on) a substance produced by cells infected by viruses that prevents viruses from spreading by interfering with their reproduction

lichen (lī′ kən) a fungus and cyanobacteria tightly intertwined

microorganisms (mī′ krō or′ gə niz′ əmz) organisms that are too small to be seen with the unaided eye

mitosis (mī tō′ sis) the process of cell division where the nucleus divides into two nuclei containing identical genetic material and the cell divides into two equal-sized cells

model (mod′ əl) a mental image of what something is like, or an object that has enough of the characteristics of what is being modeled that a scientist can learn from it, or use it to explain something that's not easy to see or understand

molds (mōldz) a group of organisms classified in the Kingdom Fungi that usually resemble fuzzy mounds

monerans (mə nîr′ ənz) one-celled organisms that lack a nucleus and organelles and are classified in the Kingdom Monera

mushroom (mush′ rüm′) a fungus that belongs to a group of fungi that includes common mushrooms, rusts, smuts, and bracket fungi

mycelium (mī sē′ lē əm) a mesh of intertwined hyphae

nucleus (ńu′ klē əs) the part of the cell that contains the hereditary material

organelles (ôr′ gə nəlz′) cell parts found in the cytoplasm of the cell, such as chloroplasts

pasteurization (pas′ chə ri zā′ shən) the process of heating food to kill microorganisms

penicillin (pen′ ə sil′ in) an antibiotic produced by the fungus *Penicillium*

photosynthesis (fō′ tə sin′ thə sis) the process in which plants use light energy to produce food

problem statement (prob′ ləm stāt′ mənt) a question to be answered by an experiment, the first step in a scientific method

producers (prə dü′ sərz) organisms that make food by the process of photosynthesis

protein (prō′ tēn) a substance that partially makes up cells and viruses

protists (prō′ tistz) one-celled organisms with nuclei and organelles

protozoan (prō′ tə zō′ ən) a protist that consumes food like animals

pseudopod (sü′ də pod′) an extension of the cytoplasm of a cell, used to move or obtain food

respiration (res′ pə rā′ shən) the process by which cells release energy from food for their life activities

scientific method (sī ən tif′ ik meth′əd) a process by which scientists gather information and test their ideas in an organized way

sexual reproduction (sek′ shü əl rē′ prə duk′ shən) the combination of the hereditary material of two parent organisms to produce an offspring with new hereditary material

simple organisms (sim′ pəl ôr′ gə niz′ əmz) one or many-celled organisms that may have characteristics of plants or animals, but have a less complex structure, and some unique characteristics

slime molds (slīm mōldz) protists that resemble amoebas during part of their life cycle but form reproductive structures that produce spores under some conditions

spirilla (spī ril′ə) spiral-shaped bacteria

spores (spôrz) reproductive cells that produce new organisms without being fertilized

sporozoans (spôr′ ə zō′ ənz) a group of protozoans that feed off of living organisms and form a type of reproductive cell called a spore

stigma (stig′ mə) a part of a euglena that contains a material that is sensitive to light and allows the organism to "sense" the direction of a light source

stromatolites (strō mat′ əl ītz) mounds or thick mats that form in the ocean, are made of layers of cyanobacteria and sediments, and are partially or completely fossilized

vaccine (vak sēn′) a dead or weakened virus or bacteria that causes your immune system to produce antibodies against an invading substance such as a virus or bacterial toxin

variable (vâr′ ē ə bəl) a factor that can cause a change in an experiment

virus (vī′ rəs) a particle made up of hereditary material and protein, that has some characteristics of both living and nonliving things, and reproduces only within a living cell

water molds (wô′ tər mōldz) a type of fungus, related to mildews, that may be one-celled or multicellular strands, decomposes dead organisms in moist environments or feeds on living organisms

white blood cell (wīt blud sel) a cell found in the bloodstream that destroys microorganisms or substances that are not part of the body

yeasts (yēstz) a group of one-celled fungi

INDEX

CREDITS